Building Spec Homes Profitably

The Professional's Guide

Kenneth V. Johnson

Building Spec Homes Profitably

The Professional's Guide

- Ensuring Profits on Every Home

- Building on Time and Under Budget

- Marketing Using Proven, Lower Cost Techniques

Kenneth V. Johnson

RS**Means**

Copyright 1995
Construction Publishers & Consultants
63 Smiths Lane
Kingston, MA 02364-0800
(781) 422-5000

The editors for this book were Suzanne Morris, Douglas Harder, and Allen Trellis. The managing editor was Mary Greene. The production manager was Helen Marcella. The production coordinator was Marion Schofield. Composition was supervised by Karen O'Brien. The book and cover were designed by Norman R. Forgit.

Printed in the United States of America

13

Library of Congress Catalog Number 95-138900

ISBN 0-87629-357-7

 Reed Construction Data

Dedicated to my son, Erik and his wife, Barbara, in appreciation for many hours of advice and editing assistance, and to my wife, Donna Marie, for her secretarial work and support.

Kenneth V. Johnson
DBA Ridgeline Homes, West Bend, Wisconsin

Table of Contents

Foreword

Building homes on speculation can be a rewarding career for those who have the energy and motivation, and who become knowledgeable and skilled in its many aspects. The successful spec home builder enjoys substantial independence, while using his or her abilities to produce an important product that will enhance people's lives. If it is such an attractive field, why don't more people make a successful career of spec building? The fact is, few spec builders are able to remain in the business outside of periods of economic prosperity. It takes professionalism, knowledge, dedication, and follow-through on the details to install and maintain a system that will ensure profitability even in poor economic climates.

Building Spec Homes Profitably offers sound guidance that can be obtained only from an experienced professional. The author's thorough and candid coverage of both business and project management issues rings true and offers important insights—even to seasoned spec builders. From an overview of the advantages of spec building to discussions of financing, market research, site selection, value engineering, and scheduling/supervision, the book gives spec builders crucial information in a "user-friendly" format. The three keys to success—location, floor plan, and value—are examined, as are many other important features of this business. The "Planning for Profit and Continuity" section provides valuable advice on long-term planning for a winning business. Case studies throughout the book allow readers to benefit from the experiences of a veteran spec builder.

Builders are fortunate to have this resource, which will give them a significant advantage in a challenging but tremendously rewarding career. This is the book to read if you are dreaming of either being a builder or having a home built for you.

Douglas Harder
President, Mountain West Home Builders, Inc., Monument, Colorado

Preface

This book is written primarily for the small-volume builder of speculative homes. Firms starting ten homes or less per year account for two thirds of the membership of the National Association of Home Builders. Builders who have built only homes on contract for owners may find enough information in this book to boost their confidence enough to try one or more homes on speculation. Realtors can benefit from reading about builders' problems and solutions. The general public can become both better builder clients and more informed buyers and sellers of the several homes that they will probably own in a lifetime. Almost every home buyer is concerned with resale value; they will find much about that subject in this book.

Throughout the book, I have included many actual experiences in the form of "Case Studies." As you are reading this book, you should be aware that all of the dollar values presented in the case studies are from past years. Most of the studies reflect experiences and costs from the 1970s and 1980s, although there are some from the 1960s and the 1990s. Because of this, and because specific costs and methods can vary greatly in different locations, you may find that the particular dollar values or techniques presented don't correspond with your own experience. Nevertheless, these accounts reflect the "real life" situations faced by spec builders nationwide. The lessons learned contain helpful information about solving problems, avoiding mistakes, and ensuring successes.

The spec builder, especially a novice, is likely to run into myriad complications and difficulties. The floor plan of the spec home may not appeal to a broad market. The exterior design may be a style that was popular twenty years ago. On the other hand, everything about the design of the home may be fine, but the builder's costs may run five to ten percent above the competition's. The building site may have location, lot configuration, or terrain problems. Speculating in real estate can be a tough experience for amateurs, and speculative home building is largely a real estate venture. Avoiding and solving problems such as these, and more, are a large part of what this book is about.

As there are so many facets of profitable spec home building presented in this book, it would be difficult, if not impossible, for you to apply all of them to your first spec home. For example, many of the techniques applied to the most cost-effective projects require a level of familiarity with the region, local labor, and material sources that can only be gained over time and with significant research. Therefore, if you are just starting out, you would do well to generally follow the conventional approach of successful builders in your area. Soon you can incorporate more, and eventually all, of the principles set forth in this book—to achieve the best possible profits on the most saleable houses.

To make optimum use of this book, you should have some familiarity with home building, either through actual experience or through reading and observation. Some knowledge of, or experience with, construction financing and real estate transactions would also be helpful in fully appreciating some of the discussion in these areas.

As you will learn early in the book, the three most important factors in the profitable spec home venture are location, value, and floor plan. With these three elements in place, you'll have a winner every time. If you can keep these three factors in focus from the beginning of your efforts, the selling price of the finished product will be "money in the bank" from the start of construction.

The Content of this Book

Following is a brief description of each of the chapters in this book. Throughout the book, I have included many personal examples of both failures and successes to illustrate the various facets of spec home building. My goal is to provide you, the reader, with enough information to minimize risks and maximize profits.

Chapter 1 presents an overview of the problems, solutions, and advantages of building on speculation. Chapter 1 also includes a complete case study—from lot purchase to closing—of a home that sold profitably during a slow market.

Chapter 2 explains the financial analysis of the spec home venture, including cost ratios, profit margins, and overhead. These essential preliminary steps come before the selection of a site or plan.

Chapter 3 is all about market research: affordability, market segments, buyer profiles, popular design elements and floor plans, and competitive analyses.

Chapter 4 covers the process of site selection. The discussion includes issues such as purchasing land, zoning, architectural controls, location, soils and drainage, building permits, and recognizing unique sites and bargains.

Chapter 5 concerns topics related to design and value engineering, including design efficiency, working drawings, floor plans, orientation, curb appeal, and interior atmosphere.

Chapter 6 covers lists, bids, and purchasing. Purchasing strategies, labor selections, and bids are all addressed, as well as buying quality materials or labor for less than your competitors.

Chapter 7 discusses the variety of issues related to construction financing and insurance.

Chapter 8 presents the topics of scheduling and supervision, including obtaining building permits, expediting, supervising, and scheduling. Chapter 8 also discusses ideas for completing the construction of a home more quickly.

Chapter 9 is about marketing—gaining exposure through advertising and other channels, using low-cost marketing techniques, working with brokers, and more.

Chapter 10 concerns events and issues after the sale of the spec home—the closing, builder warranties, title insurance, and callbacks. The chapter provides advice for minimizing these costs and lowering exposure to liability.

Chapter 11 covers paperwork, forms, and long-term planning—the essential ingredients to a successful business venture. The discussion addresses writing a business plan, organizing paperwork, determining business philosophies, and spotting industry trends.

Kenneth V. Johnson
West Bend, Wisconsin
1994

Chapter 1
Introduction

The goal of this book is to address each of the business management concerns involved in the successful production and sale of a "spec" home. These concerns include market research; site selection; design and value engineering decisions; purchasing and expediting methods; and low-cost, high-exposure marketing strategies. The book emphasizes creating a product that will sell profitably, regardless of the state of the economy.

In the strictest sense, the term "speculatively-built" refers to a home that is not constructed under contract for a particular client. Because spec homes are started, and often finished, before they are sold, the practice of spec building is inherently more risky than building under contract. By following the guidelines discussed in this book, however, you can dramatically reduce this risk. These principles can also help the owner-builder to maximize the financial gain from a personal residence.

The case studies presented throughout the book relate experiences that will help you not only to understand the business but also to become aware of the many "pot holes" in the road to managing a successful spec building career.

The Importance of Business Skills

During a boom, when almost any builder can build a home on speculation and sell it easily at a good profit, everyone seems to be active, including many temporary part-time builders — the carpenter, the plumber's son, the title insurance company executive, the airline pilot, the high school teacher, plus many existing customer/contract builders. Because of the easy entry into this field, the market is soon flooded with poorly-conceived products. I have seen 30-year-old plans built on unattractive sites sell readily during booms. Overall, however, home building activity is cyclical over many years. Soon the boom comes to its inevitable conclusion. Many new builders acquire some bad habits during these times and fail to survive in the more normal market that follows.

These speculative builders often suffer from the following mistakes:
• Poor market research
• Poor site research and selection

- Poor planning of gross profits
- Inadequate architectural sophistication for the given market
- Costly purchasing mistakes
- Ignorance of the value of marketing
- Overpayment for financing, title insurance, property taxes, attorneys, etc.
- Inability to admit mistakes, minimize losses, and move on

Successful builders have developed good business management skills that are unique to spec home building. They plan each project as though the market could deteriorate before the home is ready for sale. If you understand this principle, you can continue building on speculation during almost any economic conditions.

For example, a very successful builder in California started operations during the bottom of the Great Depression. After several decades of popularity, the one-story bungalow and Craftsman styles had run their course. The builder introduced a new one-story design, known as the ranch or rambler style, which the market quickly accepted. A builder does not need to develop a new style to earn a profit on a spec home during difficult times, however. This book will help you to realize just what needs to be done to profit from the building of spec homes, during both good and bad times.

Three Keys to Success

If a new home can provide three key features for the prospective buyer, it will sell readily every time. These three points may seem simple and obvious, but the lack of attention to the simple and obvious is often the undoing of a complex project.

"Location, Location, Location"

A home should be built so that the surrounding homes and community will bring its value to the highest possible level. If you do not fully appreciate the importance of location, you should read and learn as much as possible from real estate books and professionals. Chapters 3 and 4 also cover the importance of location in more detail.

Floor Plan

A good floor plan is one that is popular in the local market. Some of the characteristics of a favorable floor plan are:
- Efficient and sensible traffic pattern
- Efficient use of floor space
- Allocation of space between various rooms that is in proportion to needs and popularity
- An entry that provides a pleasant and welcoming experience
- Windows that are placed to provide attractive natural light in the best locations
- All of the types of rooms or living spaces, if not more, that the local market expects within the asking price range

Chapter 5 includes a more detailed discussion of these and other design issues.

Value

Value is the most important of the three points. True value will always sell. Buyers often understand value better than sellers and builders do. A buyer may express desire for a fourth or fifth bedroom, an extra-large formal dining area to accommodate an heirloom dining set, or a home with some brick on the exterior. But show the same buyer a home that fits his basic needs and is a better value than the previous 20 homes he has inspected, and he will make an offer.

Your goal as a spec builder should be to efficiently produce a desirable new home for an adequate profit. This is done by providing better value than the competition of new and nearly-new housing stock.

Questions and Answers about Spec Building

If you are contemplating a career (or an experiment) in spec building, you undoubtedly have many questions. Probably the most important ones are: Will I be able to sell the home for an adequate profit? Will that profit be at least equal to what I would gain if I built the same home on contract for an owner of a piece of land?

Why Build Spec?

Let's consider the problems of building a home on contract for an owner of a site. Often the owner has overpaid for a site with difficult terrain or subsoil problems, poor location, or unsuitability to her desired home design. The owner may select a home plan that is awkward or has very narrow resale market appeal, or is expensive to construct and beyond her resources. If she selects a builder's model, she will often make many changes to the original plan and specifications, both before and during construction. These changes are usually disruptive and expensive. The builder's experience with the client can become frustrating, adversarial, and physically and emotionally draining. This often happens because a small builder cannot shield himself from an owner who may be critical or full of ideas for changes in the plans and specifications.

On the other hand, buyers of spec homes typically see the home in its final form and are satisfied with it—otherwise they wouldn't purchase it. During the warranty period (one or more years after completion), spec buyers are not as likely to be critical—they have not been through the construction process with its delays, unpredictable weather, agonizing decisions, and perhaps disappointment in not being able to afford everything they desired.

Changes to a builder's model often lower the final value of the home, or do not return the added cost. The result is often a distorted design, full of cost overruns, that doesn't appeal to a broad market. Imagine the auto industry operating in this way. Buyers would be all over the offices and plant during the design and construction of their custom and semi-custom cars. Changes such as "Make the doors two inches wider" or "Lower the window adjoining the left rear seat" would be prevalent. Imagine the cost both to the auto industry and to the public. Yet this is how a large segment of the home building industry operates.

Thousands of builders promote themselves as "custom builders." The word "custom" has become distorted to include almost any type of production. Lately even production builders have been encouraging more and more buyer customization of the final product. Many builders report that each custom home has an average of forty change orders before completion. You should be responsive to the market, but with good judgment.

For most of the general public, being closely involved in the design and construction management of their home is a very expensive and stressful undertaking. Over the years, I've built almost as many homes on contract as on speculation. Overall, I've achieved better long-term relations with the buyers of my spec homes than with those who hired me to build their design or our design on their site. Four to six months is a long time to be "married" to your client during the building process.

Case Study:
Building on Contract for an Industrial Engineer

Here's one example of working with a buyer on contract in Colorado. The client, who was an industrial engineer, noticed some hairline cracks in the surface of the fresh concrete footings at his new home site. He accused us of using an inferior concrete mix. I knew those hairline cracks were only surface deep, caused by a dry, hot wind that blew over Colorado on the day the footing was placed. The footing strength was as specified, but I could not convince the client of this. I finally had to hire a licensed structural engineer to inspect and report on the footing. Only then was I able to reassure the client. Later, he was convinced that we had omitted the cabinet doors from the dining side of his island kitchen counter. We had followed the client's plans, which he had drafted himself. As it turned out, he had been unaware of the professional practice of using dotted lines to indicate doors on the opposite side of a cabinet elevation.

Case Study:
Building on Contract for an Irrational Client

Here is an experience that illustrates the type of clients that builders may encounter when building on contract. Throughout the course of building a house for "Mr. and Mrs. Jones," we had many encounters that demonstrated to me how irrational these clients were. The first of these encounters occured when Mrs. Jones told me that she didn't think her husband would like the *house number* that the city assigned the home when the building permit was obtained. (Mr. and Mrs. Jones divorced soon after taking occupancy of their customized "dream home.")

What are the Advantages to Spec Building?

Building homes on speculation often offers better working conditions than building on contract. One reason is that the project can begin at a time that is convenient for you. Also, besides the extra effort involved in dealing with a contract client, dealing with the client's lender for loan approval and the periodic release of funds adds more hours to the process.

Spec home building offers many options in terms of your own lifestyle. You can work 52 weeks a year or 26. You can build several homes during the warm months and spend winters relaxing (or working on smaller projects) in a mild climate. Or take a vacation after the sale of each home. Even if you have one or two homes under construction at all times, you can plan a getaway for a less demanding time of the construction cycle. Chapter 11 discusses some of the other characteristics of a spec builder's lifestyle.

Perhaps most importantly, consider the differences in gross profits between contract and spec building. In general, contract building gross profits are only 60-80 percent of those experienced in spec building. Why? Because spec building is a more efficient way of producing a home. If you are successful, you will be compensated for an increased level of risk and land purchasing expertise. The actual level of risk can be decreased, however, as you gain more experience and knowledge.

Here's another question you may ask: Why would a low-volume builder want to work at building on contract? Lack of capital, lack of expertise, and lack of confidence in the business aspects of speculative construction are likely reasons.

The pre-construction process involved in building for a client includes visiting models, going over plans, estimating, obtaining owner financing, and so forth—a process that often consumes more calendar time than the actual construction. In most cases, the builder is forced to estimate or execute inappropriate or unreasonable requests that are made at the worst times. The contract builder is also often subjected to unjust criticism: almost every family has an "expert" who is on hand during construction to point out one imaginary flaw after another.

Not all contract building clients are difficult, of course. The best clients are those who have gone through the building process once or twice before and know that absolute perfection in plans, specifications, or construction at an affordable price is impossible to obtain. They know that no matter how many homes they build or who builds them, there will always be things they would improve upon if they could begin over.

As a spec builder, you have more control over timing, project types, costs, subcontractors and suppliers, and work-related stress. You can enjoy pride and satisfaction from building creativity rather than frustration with the client. In the end, usually a more attractive, lower-cost product is added to the nation's housing stock: All these benefits and approximately 50 percent more gross profit! This 50 percent additional gross profit often translates, for example, into a $24,000 gross profit versus a $16,000 gross profit on a 2,000-square-foot home.

What is the Market for Spec Homes?

A large portion of the home-buying public is aware of the agonies and cost overruns involved in hiring a builder or subcontractors to produce their dream home. They have heard about others' bad experiences. Yet they recognize the carefree first years of new home ownership, the luxury of newness, the price appreciation resulting from their own decorating and landscaping, and the increasing desirability of their new home's location. They know a new home offers faster and more profitable resale, should they need to relocate in a few years.

A prospective buyer will purchase a spec home when he is attracted to one that has the three indispensable attributes discussed earlier: location, floor plan, and value. He might like to build a custom home on contract to satisfy his every desire, but he doesn't have the time or the money to do it. This is the market that is always there, waiting for your product.

Chapter 3 includes a more detailed discussion about market research for spec building.

How Important is Affordability?

Affordability is a more significant factor in the purchase of a home than in the purchase of any other consumer item. Many people indulge themselves in various consumer items they can't afford, such as expensive clothing, cars, and entertainment. The highest quality—affordable or not—is often placed within reach by loans and credit cards. However, when prospective buyers apply for a home mortgage loan, their income comes under greater scrutiny. Many cannot buy into the most affluent suburb or afford expensive roofing materials or masonry exteriors, for example.

Often real estate salespeople have a long list of qualified buyers who will consider any new home up to a certain price level—$150,000, for example. For this group of buyers, new homes in the $135,000–$150,000 range probably sell much faster than those in the $175,000–$190,000 range. If the small builder produces a home that sells in an affordable, high-demand price range, he will appeal to many out-of-town transferees as well as the local market. Typically, these buyers will not consider lower-priced "bare bones" starter homes or more expensive older homes that need extensive repair or remodeling. In a large part of America, the affordable "move-up" home in the lower end of the market is usually in the 1,800–2,300-square-foot range. In the larger-home market, the number of families who are financially qualified declines dramatically and may be vulnerable to rises in interest rates. Many affluent home buyers were created during the '80s. This group is generally interested in homes that are 3,000–5,000 square feet or larger.

How Can I Compete with the High-Volume Builder?

High-volume builders are usually not effective in metropolitan areas where demand for new single-family homes is under 6,000 units per year. Even in a market dominated by large firms, however, low-volume builders can find single-family lots in good locations that the larger companies have either overlooked or cannot handle with ease. Small builders can also change locations or designs much faster than large firms can. Some markets are dominated by custom building or by duplicating builders' models on the buyer's lot. The small spec builder who is efficient, market-wise, and able to cut costs without cutting quality can sell a home in any of these markets.

The New Generation of Builders

As mentioned earlier in this chapter, in recent years builders whose backgrounds have nothing to do with construction are increasing in number. Builders still enter from the ranks of carpenters and other building tradespeople, but many of the new builders entering the industry come from traditional white-collar, college-educated professional backgrounds: former lawyers, economists, engineers, tax accountants, even meteorologists.

Success in homebuilding depends on skills that have nothing to do with swinging a hammer. As Ralph Waldo Emerson said, "Cultivated labor drives out brute labor." Operating a building company calls for professional business skills. Many tradespeople can become good spec builders, but they too should acquire architectural design expertise and real estate knowledge along with the required business skills. Without this background, a builder's product is often poorly located, over-improved, or built from an unpopular, dated design. The workmanship may be superior, but workmanship is not enough to save a home from market rejection. On the other hand, many builders from non-building professional backgrounds are accustomed to seeking the advice of experts to avoid errors. A builder can delegate all of his mental and physical tasks except two: selecting the site and deciding what is to be built on that site.

Case Study:
Building a Spec Home During a High-Interest-Rate Period

A golf course subdivision addition at a private country club was started during the late 1970's in an affluent suburb in southeast Wisconsin. Because of a fairly severe local recession and high interest rates, only 25–35 percent of the available lots were built on during the first five to seven years. The 100-foot-wide, one-third-acre lots were offered at $30,000 and higher for sites not fronting the golf fairways. Almost all the sold lots had been purchased by either local builders or the general public. Several 3,000–4,500-square-foot executive-style homes were built on the fairways. Minimum size requirements were reasonable on the non-fairway lots and several 2,200–2,500-square-foot and larger homes had already been built.

The lowest-priced lot was just under $30,000. It was flanked by an all-brick ranch of about 2,000 square feet and a two-story colonial-style home of 2,400 square feet. The rear or north side of this flat, treeless site adjoined a 5–10 acre wooded parcel. The view south from this site was of a 3,500-square-foot traditional English-style home on a well-landscaped, large corner lot. I had approached the subdivision developer earlier about enlarging a starter-home design for his subdivision. To my surprise, he seemed quite willing to approve a 2,000-square-foot home. When I was ready to purchase the lot, I tried to buy it for even less than the very reasonable asking price, but the developer claimed his bank/partner would not allow it. However, he returned 3 percent of the price to me as one-half of a typical sales commission because I had a real estate broker's license. We then discussed market demand in various price ranges. As this developer was also building homes on contract and duplex condos on spec at the other end of the golf course, his observations were quite valuable. At that time he believed that buyer demand diminished greatly after the new home price exceeded $125,000; he felt that point was sometimes $115,000.

I had $120,000 in mind as the selling price for the proposed spec home. The lot cost fit in nicely, as it was slightly less than the then-prudent ratio of 25 percent fully improved lot cost to the complete home sale price. My preliminary building design began with these goals: (1) a 2,000-square-foot, two-story home with three bedrooms and two and one-half baths; (2) cedar lap siding exterior throughout and no expensive masonry (cheaper aluminum siding was frowned upon by the developer); (3) an attached two-car garage, which was entered from the end so two home-like garage windows faced the street; (4) a full basement, but with a laundry room on the first floor; (5) some striking architectural design features on both the exterior and the interior.

As the plans reached the working drawing stage, the home took the form of a "reverse salt box": a 7"/12" roof pitch with full two-story wall in the rear, and off-center roof ridge, and a long, sloping roof to the first-floor ceiling level toward the street. This long slope was broken by a "through the eaves" dormer over the transomed living room windows. The only second-story space facing the street contained one bedroom and appeared as a huge dormer in this sloping roof. The two garage windows also had hip-roofed, "through-the-eaves" dormers over them.

Ordinarily, a spec builder should not design something as complicated as this because the framing lumber and carpentry labor becomes too expensive. The garage trusses had an off-centered ridge with longer upper chords to the street for a low sheltering roof appearance. Most of the house roof also used trusses, over the large bedroom-dormer and across the entire rear of the second story, where they spanned from the exterior rear wall to a center bearing wall. The remainder of the roof was framed with 2" x 8" rafters, the upper ends of which joined the trusses at the center bearing wall. This roof shape also allowed for a dramatic soaring foyer, including a 180-degree-turn stairway, a partial hall balcony, and skylights. The roof line also allowed for a vaulted ceiling over the fireplace and living room.

The second floor contained the master bedroom with a walk-in closet and a vanity at the end of a small bay with a shower and toilet behind. Two other bedrooms and a bath were also on the second floor. The first floor included a den adjacent to the entry foyer and half bath. There was no family room in this design, but I tried to compensate with a country kitchen-dinette long enough to accommodate a small loveseat. This kitchen also included a paneled bay window with a built-in seat. Open to the living room and adjacent to the kitchen was a formal dining area. Through the dinette patio door was a 200-square-foot wood deck.

Because of a slow market with high interest rates, I added several cost-effective custom items: 2" x 6" exterior stud walls to conserve heat; two member crown moldings, hardwood floors, and a small bookcase in the den; an isolated peninsula range hood, built of wood and sheetrock; mock beams across the kitchen ceiling; double-entry doors to the master bedroom; and six-panel doors — but only on the first floor, where visible from the foyer. The total added cost here was $2,000–$3,000. I felt this was a reasonable price for items that would differentiate my product from the competition.

What should have been changed in this design? First, the value of the 2″ x 6″ exterior wall was not appreciated by the buyers, given the extra cost of carpentry, lumber, window jambs, added insulation, and lost floor space. They didn't seem interested in monitoring their heating costs for comparison, despite their interest in other numbers. However, the first-floor den proved quite popular. One prospect wanted an office in the home where clients could enter right off the foyer. The master bedroom had a long common wall adjacent to a child's bedroom. I had done this before. No one had ever commented about this lack of privacy, but I swore to maintain complete master bedroom privacy in the future. I also felt the double entry doors in the master bedroom provided less privacy than one door. No one mentioned the lack of a definite family room, but I was concerned about it and realized that I could have built one behind the garage with almost a full view of the kitchen-dinette. However, the added cost would have pushed the price past the demand range.

The final plans were approved by the developer, a subdivision architectural committee representative residing nearby, and the municipal architectural board. Construction began with a culvert I installed myself. Thirty minutes of hand shovel work along a string line prepared an even area into which a lumber delivery truck dropped a steel culvert pipe that came to rest at the ditch water flow line. A load of crushed rock was dumped on top, to be spread by the basement excavator's backhoe before it crossed over the lot line to begin excavation work. Thus I earned $145 for an hour of labor.

I undertook several other jobs during construction normally completed by subcontractors: the design and drafting of plans; installation of concrete footings; the interior fireplace brick facing and hearth, where I experimented with a new fireplace treatment; the wood deck; basic interior carpentry, which I shared with a more skilled part-time carpenter; interior painting and staining; and general clean-up work. A father-son team subcontracted the basement construction at reasonable cost.

The rough or framing carpentry contractor gave me a good price. He'd worked for the developer on larger luxury units and proved to be skilled and efficient. Despite this, a single second-story wall raised late on a Friday succumbed to strong winds over the weekend. On Sunday morning, I learned this entire section had blown into the neighbor's driveway overnight. The carpenter responded to the situation and debris was removed and ready for rebuilding on Monday, all paid for by builder's risk insurance.

By spring our progress was accelerating, and I checked my near-final costs of land, materials, and subcontractors; my labor value; my own fund's financing costs; interim taxes; and insurance; and found them to be about $96,000 — just $1,000 over the original budget and within the 2 percent maximum overrun range.

To sell the house, I ran a few small classified ads in the metropolitan paper without much response. Small signs tacked to various trees and telephone poles nearby directed people past the home. A broker friend and I had an oral agreement regarding use of brokerage service: three percent to brokers who contacted me directly; 4 percent to her to cover other brokers working through her; and 5 percent if the full service of metropolitan multiple listing was used. Several brokers stopped in during the last four weeks of construction, some with prospective buyers in tow. Most brokers stayed away because of the lack of a written listing contract.

When the house was far enough along—with countertops and most woodwork installed—I held a Sunday afternoon open house. Early in the afternoon a family of four stopped in for a short visit. They lived in a nearby suburb and had recently joined the country club. After eating dinner in the clubhouse, they accidentally drove into the subdivision, not realizing new homes were being built there. They returned again later in the afternoon to measure the rooms for their furniture. They owned a home that was not on the market; I decided to try to move them into action. The price of my product was $120,000. I told them that very soon, I would consider listing it with a full service broker for closer to $125,000, but if they could write a contract within a week for $115,000 it was theirs. Before the week was out, we had a very good sales contract drawn for $115,000. They had a solid income, a large down payment, and no contingency on the sale of their old home.

The closing for the buyer's mortgage company was at a downtown law firm. I was careful to ensure the real estate tax was prorated fairly. Otherwise, the basis of proration would have been for a fully completed home, as if all construction were final on the previous January 1, the date for tax assessment in Wisconsin. I also requested that I be paid with a cashier's check as called for in all real estate sale contracts (cash or certified funds). I would not accept a check on their law firm's account. Because no construction loan was involved, my proceeds were near the sale price and a cashier's check would allow me to start earning a good daily money market return beginning the day of the closing, not several days later when their check cleared.

I earned a return of about 20 percent. Total gross profit, before my general overhead of vehicles, telephone, insurance, etc., was about $20,000 or about 17 percent of gross sales. The value of my own labor was about $3,800 additional. If a broker had brought in the buyer, she probably would have obtained a price about 3 percent higher, or $119,000. The gross profit (including sales cost) would have been closer to 20 percent—right on target. The broker services may have cost $6,000. Without the broker, the buyer saved $4,000 and I saved $2,000—a sensible resolution. The closing took place very soon after all construction was complete—no time, money, or worry was lost waiting for a sale.

Summary

This chapter has provided an overview of home building from the perspective of a low-volume builder. The case study you just read covers several elements of spec building that will be discussed in more detail in later chapters. The remaining chapters of the book will cover the chronological step-by-step business duties and decisions involved in speculative construction. Chapter 2 concerns one of the main reasons we're in the business: gross profit margins.

Note: Whenever a building boom forces demand to outstrip supply and prices to rise rapidly, some of the financial guidelines and ratios outlined in this book may have to be disregarded. The builder's product will sell at a good profit, despite the fact that some general limits have been exceeded – provided a buyer is located before the boom ends.

Key Points

- Successful spec builders possess good management skills that are unique to spec home building.
- Many new spec builders come from traditional white-collar backgrounds. Both tradespeople and new builders with white-collar backgrounds who enter the field need good business skills, design experience, and real estate knowledge.
- Advantages to a career in spec building include the ability to begin a project at a time that's convenient for you, to choose your own designs and construction schedules, and to earn higher gross profits than contract builders.
- If you are a small builder, you can often find lots in good locations that the larger firms have overlooked, and can change locations or designs more quickly than large firms can.
- Good location, floor plan, and value are essential to the success of a spec home. Consider these points before selecting any land or home design for spec construction.
- To appeal to the local market as well as transferees, a spec home must be affordable within a high-demand price range.
- A builder who is efficient, market-wise, and able to cut costs without cutting quality can sell a home in virtually any market.

Chapter 2
Feasibility, Margins, & Ratios

The topic of profit appears early in this book. Why? It might seem more appropriate near the end. Unless a builder has a good grasp of the gross profit margin needed to survive in this business, it will be difficult to select a building site and a home to be built on it. The spec builder must work backward from the target sale price of the proposed home, include an adequate gross profit, determine the construction budget and financing cost, and ascertain whether enough funds are left over for purchase of the site. This process is an important part of your feasibility study. Don't expect to add a gross profit last, as an afterthought, or expect that a profit will occur automatically.

"Profits taken for granted are like friends taken for granted—they are seen less often."—Anonymous

Gross profit percentages or dollar amounts are seldom discussed thoroughly and adequately by small builders. Quite often these builders are unaware of what items belong under gross profit. They often mingle the value of their own on-site construction labor with gross profits. Perhaps previous gross profits have varied so widely from home to home that they don't know what is necessary or normal. Your gross profit margin must be large enough to ensure adequate personal income over the long term—ten years or more.

First, let's consider some gross profits encountered in contract building. Some custom, build-for-client builders might mention $5,000 and 10 percent over direct hard costs, or a 15 percent markup, to describe their expected gross profit. A carpenter contractor who acted as the general contractor on a motel construction for a large nationwide chain reported receiving a 6.5 percent gross profit markup for his services. One recent advertisement in a large West Coast city proclaimed the builder would custom build for actual costs plus 19 percent or first meeting cost estimates plus 19 percent, whichever is less. Spec building gross profits need to be higher than contract building margins of gross profit because the end sale price is at some risk and because careful research goes into site selection and design of the home.

Composition of Gross Profit, Overhead, and Net Profit

Gross profit includes the cost of market research; office, phone, and vehicle costs; purchasing, expediting, and supervision costs; bookkeeping and secretarial costs; marketing costs; and, of course, the net profit. Without adequate gross profit to cover all of the above overhead costs and a net profit, a spec-home building career will soon end. About 25 percent of all home builders fail during a recession.

Here are three definitions of the net profit, the most important yet most volatile part of the overall gross profit:

- The builder's payment for the risk of losing money, but more likely the risk of losing the value of time spent building a spec home.
- A payment greater than the return the builder's capital would have gained in a risk-free investment, such as a U.S. Treasury Bill.
- A payment for entrepreneurship – the time and money spent to set up the business, from writing a business plan to selecting the first site and home design.

Let's identify a percentage for each of the above elements and consolidate them into a *total* net profit:

- If the builder does a good job of estimating costs, actual cost should come in as close as within 1 percent of estimated cost. Let's use 2 percent for this risk factor to be sure.
- A Treasury Bill return might be 3–6 percent annually; use 3 percent for the four to six months that might pass from the site purchase to the closing on the home.
- The cost of entrepreneurship might be estimated at 3 percent (at least).
- Total: 2 + 3 + 3 = 8 percent total *net* profit, which is part of a 18–22 percent gross profit, for example.

This is only one example. The net profit required could be calculated to suit any individual situation. The state of the local market, the competition, and the difficulties of building in a certain locale will need to be factored into the composition of net profit. In general, a net profit of 5 percent or less is too low. At that level, one small crisis or delay could eliminate all of it.

Overhead

The true overhead for any small builder is usually much larger and encompasses more items than the builder is aware of. The broad category of overhead can be divided into *production overhead* and *sales overhead*.

Production Overhead

Production overhead is comprised of the elements listed in Figure 2.1.

The costs of production overhead items – phone bills, vehicle costs, etc. – are easy to ascertain, with the exception of your own time spent as secretary, bookkeeper, purchasing agent, expediter, and construction superintendent. Here, some research is necessary. A dollar amount must be included for these hours; at an hourly rate that is comparable to what slightly larger builders are paying their employees for these services. Let's say these duties require 250-350 hours per home. Statistics indicate that the production of seven homes per year per management employee is average, for a well-run giant company that subcontracts all construction. (The figure of seven homes was derived from researching "The Value Line Investment Survey" of publicly held large home builders. This reference is available at most libraries.) That equals about 300 labor-hours per home. If seven homes per person per year is average, the numbers probably vary from five to ten homes. These figures are for the smaller end of the move-up home market. One very efficient private builder produced 100 homes annually using only 6 people—16 homes per employee. They were repeating the same design on scattered lots during the 1970s.

If you have no other records to work from, you would be wise to budget 300 hours per home, and to charge these hours at the rate paid to a skilled carpenter to arrive at a production overhead cost. For example:

300 hours x $20 per hour = $6,000
(4 percent of the sale price of a $150,000 home)

Another way to calculate this item is to determine the sales revenue of completed homes in dollars per management personnel. Many firms produce about $500,000 in revenue per employee, but some do three times that. If the total average annual cost of this type of personnel is $35,000 per year, then this portion of the overhead can be from 2–3 percent to as high as 7 percent. When you add up all the production overhead costs and divide into the annual sales, does it come into the range of 5–10 percent? Overall, the

Office	Rental of office space, or the true cost of using part of your home and garage; office furnishings and equipment; association dues and licenses; office supplies.
Office staff	General phone work; bookkeeping; general office duties (the cost for employees or the comparable value of the builder's time devoted to this work).
Phone	Separate business phone or portion of household phone, plus pay-phone calls and car phone.
Insurance	General business liability. Don't include the cost of builder's risk insurance on homes under construction. That is a direct job cost, not overhead.
Vehicle cost	True cost (not IRS allowances) of vehicles used for business only.
Purchasing, expediting, and supervision of construction	All costs for time required to research and purchase the land, design services, selection of building materials, choosing subcontractors, and coordinating the construction of the home by subcontractors. Also include the time spent on construction financing. The small builder typically does all of this work; a dollar amount must be included for these hours.

Figure 2.1 Production Overhead Items

figure representing hours per home is more accurate than sales volume per management employee because it allows for inflation.

Sales Overhead

Sales overhead includes the items shown in Figure 2.2.

A full-service real estate broker generally charges the general public a commission rate of 6 or 7 percent. I don't think a builder should have to pay this much. In general, if you are continually producing new homes that are easily saleable, you should try not to pay more than 5 percent. Volume builders, whose sales staff sell from model homes, generally have sales costs as low as 4 percent total – 2 percent for the salesperson, 1 percent for advertising, and 1 percent for the model home cost. If you sell the home without a broker, you will probably realize that a 2 percent salesperson is not overpaid. You may be able to sell directly, without advertising or expensive signage. Sales cost overhead should not be budgeted as low as 2 percent, however; between 3 percent and 5 percent should be budgeted for efficient sales cost. These numbers and percentages may not be applicable in all parts of the country. You may have to do some research of your own to ascertain the appropriate and practical percentages.

A more detailed discussion of sales overhead items appears in Chapter 9.

Net Profit and Gross Profit

Now calculate the gross profit margin and the markup required to yield that margin. An often-quoted set of ratios for overhead and profit is shown in Figure 2.3.

One builder's experience may call for 20 percent of sale price to cover overhead and profit, but the breakdown would be different: sales expenses 4 percent, general overhead 6 percent, and profit 10 percent. During very difficult times, the 20 percent margin may have to be scaled back to a 15

Cost of discounted **brokerage services.**

Advertising costs.

The value of **builder's time** as salesperson.

Legal and escrow services as needed.

Market research that is pertinent to the selection of the site and target price range.

Figure 2.2 Sales Overhead Items

8% for general overhead, including construction supervision

6% for advertising, model homes and sales

8% net profit

20% total gross profit

Figure 2.3 Ratios for Overhead and Profit

percent margin. During boom times, this margin can easily increase to 22–23 percent. The same builder's greatest margin might be about 33 percent — perhaps as a result of purchasing the lot for 30 percent below its value in a rapidly rising land market. The builder's worst gross profit margin may be as low as 0 percent — which usually occurs early in a building career. An inexperienced builder might purchase slightly difficult terrain; overpay for the lot; make some design errors in the floor plan; and/or get caught at the peak of the mortgage interest rate cycle in a local recession.

Even the housing industry giants report gross profit margin totals close to 20 percent. A 6–10 percent pre-tax net profit is a normal range for them. About 20 percent of the giants obtain 11–15 percent net profit. The gross profit margin, however, is not the same as the markup. To obtain a 20 percent gross profit margin, mark up costs 25 percent; for a 15 percent margin, mark up costs 17.64 percent; and for a 22 percent margin, mark up costs 28 percent. Often this simple mathematical fact escapes a small builder. For example, suppose the costs of land, financing, and construction equal $120,000. Mark up these costs by 25 percent: 120,000 x .25 = 30,000. To arrive at the price of the product: 120,000 + 30,000 = 150,000. Now the gross profit margin will equal 20 percent, because 30,000 is 20 percent of 150,000. Business analysis always begins by comparing overhead, profit, and any costs to the sale price of the product.

Only in the area of using prefabricated, modular, or other factory-constructed housing is the overhead and profit margin appreciably different. It is lower, of course, because costs are less volatile and the construction cycle time is shorter. On the other hand, builders who are also developing subdivision lots from raw land have larger percentages of gross profit margins — developing raw land is a more risky proposition compared to building homes.

If you are an established builder, an advisable approach is to plan for a 20–22 percent gross profit (about 25–28 percent markup on costs). Those hard costs include land and construction costs and financing costs. The only costs that are not marked up are those that are paid at sale closing, and those that are not out-of-pocket expenses at a prior time and require no administration or supervision time. Real estate sales tax paid by the seller, the current year's property tax proration, and title insurance for the buyer are examples of no-markup costs.

Direct-Cost Ratios and Variations

Direct costs involved in building spec homes include the following:
• Financing costs
• Design costs
• Ready-to-build land costs
• Construction costs

Financing costs can vary from 2 percent to 7 percent of the sale price, depending on both the builder's source of funds and current interest rates.

Most builders' financing costs will fall in the 3 percent to 4 percent range. There will be more discussion about this in Chapter 7.

Design costs include design-related market research, design and drafting costs, and printing costs for drawings. These will be covered in greater detail in Chapter 5.

The term *ready-to-build land* means that the sewer and water service to the home and an entry for the driveway are included. Historically, land costs as a percentage of the finished home package have been rising. Land costs have been inflating faster than construction costs. In the late 1940s, land costs were as low as 10 percent of the finished package. This ratio may still exist in small, stagnant communities. The most common ratio has been about 25 percent of the finished package. In recent years, this ratio seems to be heading toward 30 percent and beyond. In high-cost communities on both coasts, 33–50 percent ratios are not uncommon.

The advice of home building industry management consultants is that construction costs should be at least 50 percent of the sales price in normal markets, in order to produce enough house to offer competitive value. A 55 percent ratio would be more ideal. A 60 percent ratio is an almost impossible goal to attain — adding 20 percent for overhead and profit and 3 percent for financing would leave only 17 percent for land cost. A 55–60 percent ratio should result in strong sales.

How far you may safely stray from these general ratios is a judgment call requiring extensive experience. Based on my own experience, in general land cost is 25 percent, design/construction costs are 52 percent, financing cost is 3 percent, overhead and profit is 20 percent. The breakdown on the overhead and profit is: general overhead, including purchasing, expediting, and supervision time, 6.5 percent; sales expense, 4.5 percent; and net profit, 9 percent. This should bring in a reasonable personal income for a small builder who remains fairly busy.

There are several ways to increase net profit. Sales costs, financing costs, construction costs, and even land costs could be lowered if you find a bargain. Much of the remainder of this book will offer advice on lowering these costs without lowering value. The effort may add some hours to purchasing, expediting, or supervisory time, which will increase overhead slightly. However, office, telephone, and vehicle costs could be lower, thus compensating for the cost of extra supervision.

Other Ratios

Other ratios besides direct costs include the following:

- The ratio of on-site subcontracted labor to all construction costs
- The "one percent ratio"
- The debt-to-equity ratio

You may believe that by doing all on-site work yourself, you can make a killing on building one home. This isn't necesarily true. The total of all subcontractors' labor, including their overhead and profit, amounts to about 25 percent of all construction costs, or about $20,000 in a $150,000 home (the $150,000 price includes land and gross profit along with construction costs). That amount is less than the builder's $30,000 overhead and profit margin. Think of the tremendous increase in time and effort, as well as the increase in construction time, if you do all on-site work yourself. Changes over the years in the manufacture of the building components have diminished the amount of on-site labor required of the builder.

Next, consider the "one percent ratio." This is the goal of an accurate estimate of construction costs. The actual total costs should come within 1–2 percent of the total estimate. It is not necessary to get within 1–2 percent on each cost component, such as lumber, plumbing, windows, and so on. An estimated cost that is 5 percent too low in carpentry, for example, could be compensated for by a plumbing estimate that is 4 percent too high. By repeatedly building the same plan or similar plan, close cost estimates are possible, even as close as one-half percent of the actual cost. If you work in an area that requires a great variety of plans—because of mountain terrain, for example—competitors' profit margins will be wider to compensate for the risk of more inaccurate estimates.

The debt-to-equity ratio concerns borrowing money for the building program. A 3:1 maximum ratio is a prudent way to lower the risk. In other words, if your program requires $120,000, $30,000 of the funds should be your own, $90,000 would then need to be borrowed. Overborrowing has been the downfall of many businesses.

Figure 2.4 includes a pie chart illustrating the breakdown of the sale price of a popularly priced spec home and showing ratios of costs and margins that are recommended and attainable.

Summary

Remember to keep a 20 percent gross profit margin in mind when selecting a site or plan for a home in your targeted price range. Your survival in this business depends on financial projections of costs and gross profit, from the very beginning of each project's conception. It is always a good idea to work backward from your targeted home sale price.

At this point we are ready to research the market. What is the buyer willing to purchase and where? How expensive should the home package be? Is there a pent-up demand for a certain type of home or a certain location?

Key Points
• Without adequate gross profit to cover overhead and net profit, a spec home building business cannot survive. Your goal should be a 20 percent gross profit margin, as a minimum.

- Production overhead items include phone bills, vehicle costs, office expenses, and the purchasing, expediting, and supervision of construction.
- Sales overhead items include brokerage services, advertising, and market research.
- Direct costs involved in building spec homes include financing, design, land, and construction costs.
- The actual construction costs should come within 1–2 percent of the total estimated cost.
- A 3:1 debt-to-equity ratio is a prudent way to lower risk: in other words, if your program requires $120,000, $30,000 of the funds should be your own money, $90,000 would then need to be borrowed.
- Try not to pay more than 5 percent for a real estate broker's commission. Commissions as low as 3 percent are possible, as you will learn in Chapter 9.
- It is not cost-effective to do all—or even some—on-site work yourself.
- A pre-tax net profit of at least 8% is your goal. Some "giant" firms realize 10-12%, even though only 5% is a nationwide average.

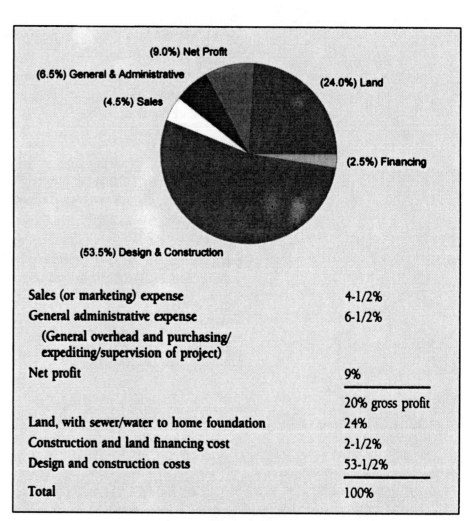

Sales (or marketing) expense	4-1/2%
General administrative expense	6-1/2%
(General overhead and purchasing/ expediting/supervision of project)	
Net profit	9%
	20% gross profit
Land, with sewer/water to home foundation	24%
Construction and land financing cost	2-1/2%
Design and construction costs	53-1/2%
Total	100%

Figure 2.4 Breakdown of the Sale Price of a Home

Chapter 3
Market Research

Before committing to a piece of land or a home design, you must determine the right place, the right house, and the right price. This is achieved by market research.

Many home buyers know much more about what is available in a general locale than the small builder does. These buyers can be more aware of the shortcomings or lack of sophistication of the floor plan and architecture of a new home than the small builder offering it. You will need to learn all that you can from the comments and criticisms of buyers. At the very least, you should be aware both of the competition and of what designs are popular in your area. Many builders can become too busy with sweat labor to do the research that leads to good planning.

The low-volume builder who does solid market research will be ahead of the competition before construction begins. In addition to ongoing observation, thorough research should be done at least four times per year. The information can be analyzed systematically at these times.

Determining Buyer Affordability and Neighborhood Limits

"Selling concentrates on the needs of the seller, marketing on the needs of the buyer." — Anonymous

The most basic goal of market research is to realize the needs of prospective home buyers. One of the first pieces of information you need is the affordability limit for the largest segment of the "move-up" buyers. This is the logical starting point for market research. At what price range should the product be aimed? Affordability is a prime factor for these buyers.

In 1994, *Professional Builder* reported a nationwide profile of move-up buyers as having a median income of $67,500 (May 1994, p. 12). The average move-up buyer was 41 years old, married, with children. The median purchase price for this group was $159,600. These statistics will vary depending on what area you build in, so it is important to do your own research using local resources for affordability limits.

Real estate brokers are often given a maximum price level to work with by prospective buyers. Most brokers will mention a figure during an initial meeting with you. If they don't, you should offer one, such as $135,000, $150,000, or $175,000. Beyond a certain level, depending on the area of the country, the number of qualified buyers dramatically decreases. The number may increase for a higher, more luxurious price range, but spec building of luxury homes is not the main thrust of this book. After speaking with several brokers, it will be obvious where the upper limits are for volume sales of new move-up homes. The National Association of Home Builders (NAHB) in Washington, D.C., may have a maximum new-home price for the median family income in your metropolitan area. For example, the most recent figure for my area is $167,000.

Other sources of information about pricing and affordability are builder association surveys, mortgage loan representatives, and real estate articles in local newspapers. Compare the annual number of sales in each price bracket and determine where sales start to noticeably decline. In certain large metropolitan areas, title companies can provide these statistics.

You should learn the median household income for both the overall metropolitan area and specific suburbs. Experts state that a home cost of 2.5 times family income is normal and 3 times family income is the upper limit. Future trends may alter this figure, however. Sales of homes costing up to 10 times family income are not unusual in northern Europe. In general, it would be wise to set the upper limit at 3 times the average household income for the community. Generally, a family is willing to pay 20–30 percent of gross monthly income for a mortgage payment. If you are working in a community with a great disparity of incomes, be careful. There may be little demand for middle-income housing, but great demand for both luxury and low-income housing.

One simple formula to estimate the upper price limit for new homes is this: To the average market value of all new homes in the entire metropolitan area, add 25 percent. This is the limit; do not build anything that costs more than this.

Researching Buyer Demographics

The wise spec builder will research the percentage of the local population in various age groups and compare these percentages with the national average. If the area is heavily weighted with very young families, there may be a demand for smaller, low-priced, or expandable homes. Single-story homes, or homes in which master bedrooms are on the first floor of a two-story home, may be in demand if there is a heavy proportion of older families.

Segmenting Buyers

One good way to study the market is to write down all the various segments of the local market (types of buyer family units) that might be interested in buying your product. For example:

• Young single professionals
• Young married couples, both employed, with no plans to have children
• Young couples with one or two children

- Couples with three to five children
- Middle-aged couples with teen-age children
- Couples with college-aged or married children
- Transferee families with children and no family ties in the area
- Single-parent families with several children
- Retired couples or couples with one spouse still working
- Older widows or widowers

The list should reflect your own area. Next to each segment a feature or two that may be in demand by that group can be added. Examples are:

- Proximity to good schools
- One first-floor bedroom for an office or room for an aged parent
- A three-car garage
- Single-level living
- Storage space for sports equipment
- An extra-large country kitchen with family room features

This list can be valuable during the design of the home. Can the market appeal of the product be enhanced by including some of these features? The more market segments that will be attracted to your product, the better.

You might also be interested in knowing what buyers will spend on options. In *Professional Builder's* 1994 Consumer Survey (July 1994, p. 104), the highest percentages of respondents were willing to spend extra money on air conditioning ($1,600–2,000); fireplaces ($3,000–6,000); upgraded carpentry ($800–1,000); and paved driveways ($500–800). Very few respondents were interested in paying for options such as bidets, saunas, and European-style cabinets. Again, depending on your area, buyers' responses to these options may vary.

Considering Location

One of your goals will be to build in a location where the surrounding homes and the community tend to bring the value of the home to its highest possible level. Of course, affordability and gross profit margins place limits on how much you can afford to pay for a good location.

Getting to Know a Community

As part of the market research effort, you should look at all the better suburban communities in your area and focus on one or two that seem well-suited to your product. This element of research involves talking to brokers, developers, and local planning departments, in addition to extensive observation. Your observation of the community should include areas that are being developed with tasteful commercial facilities (shopping, office parks, research facilities, golf courses), as well as areas with beautiful views, good transportation access, luxury housing nearby, and good parks. Get to know at least one community very well, if possible, to the extent of knowing the locations of all existing and future vacant lots, every builder operating there, the best areas, and the worst areas. One way to really know a community is to live there yourself! One very successful real estate speculator-developer was able to quote the price, history, and zoning of every building or parcel of land in downtown Dallas. He knew more about his location of operation than anyone else. A good rule of thumb is to try to stay within one hour's drive of your own home or office. Subdivisions in financial trouble may be an opportunity, but they are usually too risky.

Be frank when using brokers for market research. They can offer much information. The advice of the best real estate person in a community should not be followed blindly, however. Your own judgment is also valuable.

Case Study:
Following Experts' Advice Too Blindly

I once was discouraged by a good broker from buying an inexpensive acre that was approved for duplex condominiums. The broker felt that the adjacent motel and coffee shop was too detrimental and that only the well-accepted local condominium developer could sell in this spot. As it turned out, two brothers who were not builders purchased adjacent sites there, erected two duplexes, and obtained high rents for four condominiums that could be sold later when the market improved.

Identifying Transferee Market Locations

You can't depend only on the local population for buyers. In many markets, corporate transferees provide small builders with a good share of the buyers for their product. This buyer usually knows very little about the new area, has no friends or family there, and knows the home he or she buys may have to be resold in several years in the event of another transfer. With little available research time, the transferee will usually go directly to a broker. The transferee will usually be shown new homes only in locations that offer easy resale in future years. There may be only one or two suburbs that brokers show this future resale buyer. You should know these suburbs—they are good locations for building spec homes.

A note on the transferee market: They often prefer four bedrooms. With a guest bedroom it becomes easier to entice friends and family from far away to visit and alleviate the loneliness of their new location.

Discovering Captive Market Locations

Market research should include being aware of the "captive market" situation: in other words, a general area or specific sites that buyers are willing to sacrifice for. It may be a waterfront location, a beautiful wooded area in a rather treeless region, an exceptional view, or a pocket of unique privacy. It is possible that the competition has ignored a desirable parcel because of problems related to local or environmental officials, the owner's tax or estate status, or a widespread misconception about the property boundaries. By applying extra effort in resolving problems, you may acquire a unique, high-demand site that has no competition. Demand for a captive market location is so strong that almost anything built there will sell immediately.

Captive market situations are few and far between. You might have some success from studying aerial photos, researching tax rolls, looking through multi-listings, talking to owners and brokers, plus a bit of luck.

Avoiding High-Tax Areas

Some states have high property taxes that vary a great deal from suburb to suburb or from one school district to another. You should try to avoid the highly-taxed locations. The payment of high taxes turns off buyers and reduces the amount of their maximum monthly payment that can be applied to the price of the home. Thus the affordability level drops in such a location.

Shopping the Competition

Part of researching the proposed location includes driving around the area at least once a month, especially where builders are busy and homes are being sold. You should closely observe the offerings of competitors, especially the more successful builders — check prices, floor plans, construction quality, land values, and special amenities. It is also important to check out the nearly-new existing homes for sale, taking a camera along. It is fairly easy to estimate the size of various homes by pacing around the exterior and calculating square footage. Note exterior colors in general, enough to recognize which colors are popular. Taking notes is a good idea; you can organize and analyze them back at the office, when your investigation proceeds further with phone calls and comparisons/evaluations.

A comparison sheet created from the drive can list the following elements of each home:

- Location
- Price
- Type of floor plan
- Home size
- Number of bedrooms and baths
- Garage space
- Quality level of interior and exterior
- Lot size
- Any special features
- The best and worst features of the home

The list might also include a space for your own estimation of how a typical buyer might comment on each home. You can calculate an overall price per square foot by dividing the asking price by the amount of heated, finished living space. The home you build should be in the lower half of the overall price-per-square-foot range of the competition. Another helpful exercise is to pinpoint, on a simple graph, the competition's overall prices per square foot, together with your proposed product.

You can chart the total prices on a separate bar graph or similar visual aid, including the nearly-new resales (this competition is more important than most builders realize!). At least three-fourths of all home sales are used homes. Resales often offer beautiful landscaping and interior finishing touches, and may be highlighted by fine furniture — all factors that aid sales.

If you are a present or former building tradesperson or material salesperson, don't get too interested in a particular detail in the course of observing other homes. In general, bricklayers will pay too much attention to bricks, roofers to roofs, and so forth. A cheap set of cabinets shouldn't cloud a former cabinet maker's accurate assessment of an exceptional floor plan, for example. It is most important to see the overall picture from the viewpoint of the buyer who is nervously trying to consider the many features that will affect his or her lifestyle and finances.

You should monitor competitors whose products are very similar in price or design to the spec home you plan to build. The same goes for resale homes. Tract builders can give you information regarding the best selling prices and popular home sizes. New homes that are 50 percent more expensive can provide some ideas for features that you might include in a lower-priced home.

When starting out in a new market, you should always observe what the more successful builders are doing: what exteriors are popular; what colors, room sizes, bathrooms, and kitchens; even the interior trim, porch details, and weatherstripping. Starting over or expanding into a new market is difficult and very risky work. It should be considered only if it is the only alternative.

Finally, any area with too many homes for sale is probably not a good location for building yet another home to be sold.

Case Study:
Filling a Niche

At one time, I considered building a spec home in a community adjacent to mine, where I had not done any building for almost 20 years. One large firm built at least 50 homes per year in the location. After inspecting quite a few of their one- and two-story homes of 1,500-2,100 square feet in various stages of construction, I realized none of them had four bedrooms. I called their office, pretending to be an out-of-town transferee who was seeking a four-bedroom, two-story home. They informed me that they did not build any because there was little demand for four-bedroom homes. After losing an early sale on my previous three-bedroom spec for lack of a fourth bedroom, I knew by building a four bedroom in this new area I would fill a niche. When it was completed, my four-bedroom home had little if any four-bedroom competition. The sale went swiftly.

Researching Other Sources and Trends

Be sure to read widely and maintain contacts with the people and organizations that can aid your market research.

Magazines and Newspapers

The annual market research surveys published in large nationwide builders' magazines can be informative, but real estate is very localized and the local preferences are much more important. The *Wall Street Journal* and *USA Today* can also provide you with market research information. The 2,000-square-foot, two-and-one-half bath, two-story home is used as a standard when comparing housing costs from city to city — an indication of the popularity of this size and type.

Real Estate Publications

A recent copy of the multiple-listing real estate catalog for your area can be valuable. These are usually published every two weeks for broker members only. A broker or salesperson who feels that some business will be forthcoming from you, sooner or later, would probably give you one that would be discarded anyway. The multiple-listing catalog can provide information on numbers of sales in each price bracket, as well as illustrate the competition in the price bracket of your proposed product.

Over time the changing thickness of the multiple-listing publications provides an indication of a buyer's market (thicker) or a seller's market (thinner). The greatest time to build is when activity is just picking up after a recession. The local multiple-listing office or real estate news editor can provide information on the average time required to sell a home. This information, together with the months of available home supply, is very important. A new home should sell quickly if the supply is only enough to last no more than six months on the market. A twelve-month supply can be very bad, but even an overbuilt market can offer an opportunity to satisfy a segment of buyers that has not received much attention. For example, are there any one-story homes being offered in a two-story market? Perhaps elderly buyers are searching for some stairless homes.

Other Community Resources

The local Chamber of Commerce is a good source of information concerning the changes in the size of the housing market. They can also enlighten you as to local economic changes that will increase or decrease total employment.

Appraisers may be able to comment on the popularity of certain features in home design, but the work of appraisers generally puts them at least six months behind in the trends.

Busy home design firms are aware of the latest buyer preferences, as are kitchen and bath remodelers. If you can track the activities of leading developers over several years, trends will become evident.

Ask previous buyers of your homes why they selected your product, what they like most about the house, and what they would change.

Finally, if one community passes no-growth legislation, that may improve new building opportunities in the adjacent communities.

Trends

Trends should not be followed *too* closely. A few years ago, family rooms adjacent to living rooms seemed to be a great idea. The total area of both rooms could be used to entertain a group of guests and for quiet times, when the family was alone, the door to the living room could be closed for a cozy family room atmosphere. For several reasons, however, the separate family room/living room arrangement is now more popular. Other recent trends include the increasing popularity of having the master bedroom on the first floor with the others on the second floor, and the desire to have walking and biking trails nearby.

Budgeting for Market Research

The costs of market research, which consist mainly of your time, are part of marketing overhead. This cost should be a maximum of one-half of one percent of the sale price of the home. For example, for a $150,000 home, market research should cost approximately $750: perhaps $300 for location and target price research and $450 for design research.

Using the Computer

You may be able to devise your own system of keeping records of your market research on a computer. I don't rely on a computer for any market research or financial feasibility work—I use only a business calculator. This simple, low-tech approach was encouraged wholeheartedly by a very successful land speculator who dealt in acreages in several states. He even avoided calculators, claiming that he found that the use of such a device would weaken his mental discipline.

Summary

The goal of market research is not only to meet the competition, but to beat it. With solid information, any builder can survive and prosper even in tough times. Avoid making your market research data so complex and extensive, however, that the most important information is obscured. In any case, be sure to stay abreast of desirable locations and design features.

Now you are ready to consider the purchase of a building site.

Key Points

- One of the first steps in market research is to determine the affordability limit for prospective buyers. A home cost of 2.5 times family income is normal; 3 times is the maximum.
- To the average market value of all new homes in the metropolitan area, add 25 percent. Do not build a house that costs more than this.
- Determine the types of buyer family units in your target market and note a feature or two that might be in demand by each group. Try to make your product appeal to a number of market segments.
- Get to know at least one community very well. The best way to do this is to live there yourself.
- Stay within an hour's drive of your own home when choosing lots to build on.
- Monitor competitors whose homes are very similar in price or design to the spec home you plan to build.
- Other sources for market information include magazines and newspapers, real estate publications, the local chamber of commerce, appraisers, and previous buyers of your spec homes.
- The cost of market research should be no more than one-half of one percent of the sale price of the home.

Chapter 4
Site Selection & Purchase

The importance of careful site selection cannot be overemphasized. Quality in market research, home design, and construction execution won't compensate for a poor or overpriced site. Poor site selection may be the error that causes the most damage to net profits. This chapter includes several case studies related to site selection, most of which are my own experiences.

As I discuss later in this chapter, the site selection process includes searching for available land, narrowing the search to specific lots, and evaluating the proposed site. An evaluation of the site includes determining the value of the property and the minimum and maximum price for a home built on that property. Once you have selected the site, you will want to go forward with the purchase. Issues concerning the purchase of property are also covered in this chapter. First, however, I relate some of my personal experiences in site selection.

The Bad News: Errors in Site Selection

The following three case studies concern mistakes that were made in researching and/or selecting a site.

Case Study:
Insufficient Research in a New Community Decreases Profits

One of my early spec-building experiences was in a community beyond prudent metropolitan commuting distance, but one with a fair amount of spec building activity. I was not aware of how competitive new home prices were. One active local builder worked along with his carpenters every day. To price the home, he included only the value of his time and added five percent to all costs as a markup. My site was near his activity, and the terrain was difficult. My lot sloped downhill, as did the street fronting it. It was a "sidehill" lot. The developer had not yet installed the concrete sidewalks or street pavement (included in the lot purchase price).

I envisioned a one-story home with a walk-out daylight basement at one rear corner. I believed this feature, and the wood deck above this basement entry, would set my product apart from the competition. During excavation, we had trouble reaching solid soil and had to go deeper than normal. Later I had to haul in 700 cubic yards of fill for around the basement to allow for the future city sidewalk elevations, which I had not checked out with the city engineer's office.

Because of the steep front lawn grade, I lost an interested cash buyer who could not imagine mowing such a lawn. I eventually hired a full-commission broker. Final cost accounting revealed that the brokerage commission was larger than my remaining gross profit.

Case Study:
An Anxious Builder's Impatience Also Reduces Profits

This is a study in impatience. I had my eye on a street of $25,000 duplex lots. When I contacted the developer in late winter, I was told no offer could be considered until his partner returned from vacation. Anxious for early-spring construction, I turned to a nearby area of four duplex lots. The best price I could obtain was $26,500. This site was on a street with more traffic; and the lots faced an area zoned for commercial development as well as high-voltage electric transmission towers. A snow drift covered most of the site. In spring I discovered that the "drift" was actually earth. Extra expense was involved in hauling away almost all of the excavated basement earth to a dump site one mile away. This error in site selection, caused simply by impatience, put a 30 percent dent into my gross overhead and profit margin.

Case Study:
It Pays to Get Away Quickly from a Bad Situation

"Getting into a deal is a cinch compared to getting out." — Anonymous

Extra care must be taken when buying land in an unfamiliar area. I had been looking for a retirement home site in the Pacific Northwest. Years of searching the region led me back to a beautiful sixteen-lot subdivision of one-and-one-half-acre sites. The homes were of high quality and the sites were well developed. About half of the lots were still empty.

A broker assured us that the developer had insisted on thorough planning. Sewer service was by individual septic systems — the approval of one for my site was a contingency in our purchase agreement. Water service was extended into a service box near one corner of each lot. The water source was a subdivision well with pump house located near the developer's home.

After owning one of these lots for about one year, I decided not to build there. Shortly after putting the lot on the market, I learned that a builder/owner of one of the other lots was refused a building permit by the state Ecology and Health Department because the subdivision water system was not of a classification that would allow for more homes. The region suffered from a proliferation of private water systems, so it would take about three years for the Ecology and Health Department to inspect and reclassify the water system.

If I had contacted the local health department about this water system, instead of relying on the opinions of brokers and others, I could have avoided purchasing the site. I was fortunate to recover the purchase price through a sale to the broker after threats of a lawsuit on our behalf; my losses were only ownership, soil testing, and transaction costs.

The Good News: Positive Decisions and the Principles Involved

Although we all learn from our mistakes, it is much more pleasant work to learn from our successes. The following several case studies illustrate how good judgment and thorough research lead to wise decisions.

Case Study:
The Early Bird Catches a Good Site at a Fair Price

On my first land search in a new area, I found the earliest stage of a new development. This mountain area subdivision of two-acre lots had advanced only to the stage of tree removal for road construction. The salesperson gave me a tour of the 65 new lots. Only one had a deposit on it. Almost all of the sites were priced equally (but were not equal in terrain, views, or vegetation). I was able to select one with a fairly level building area, beautiful trees, and one of the best views of a nearby mountain peak.

Case Study:
Good Lot Locations Help to Advertise Products

A young builder constructed a model home on a street between a major thoroughfare and a "Parade of Homes" subdivision. For many visitors, driving past this home provided the easiest access to the "Parade." The builder not only sold his product, but acquired seventeen new customers for other sites—all for zero advertising cost.

Case Study:
Odd-shaped Lots can be Bargains

I purchased several pie-shaped lots at a discount in a rapidly-developing subdivision. These one-third-acre lots were very wide at the street and narrow in the rear yard. Most buyers appreciated the wide open look and extra privacy between neighbors, and still had adequate space in their undersized rear yards.

Case Study:
Difficult Sites can be Bargains, too

In a mountainous subdivision, the best remaining lot was shaped like one quarter of a circle. A stream ran along part of one interior lot line and put severe restraints on the size of a home's "footprint." By designing an L-shaped two-story house, I was able to maintain the required setbacks from the curving street and stay away from the stream. As a result, I was able to offer a unique design with a good floor plan at a very competitive price.

Case Study:
Thorough Searching Yields Good Value

During a boom period in a high-income suburb, the selection of moderately priced lots on the market was poor. I decided to call on owners of vacant lots. I drove along every road and street, and visited the city assessor's office to obtain owners' names and assessment amounts. The assessor told me others had recently tried this approach without success. However, every evening I phoned about ten land owners. At first, responses were discouraging. Finally, I had a positive reply. I drafted an offer to purchase enough land to create three well-located home sites. My land development work consisted only of surveying, obtaining city approval of the land division, paying division fees, and having the electric utility company relocate power lines underground. The sewer lines and roads had been in place for years.

The list I had compiled of vacant parcels of land and owners was a source of several purchases in the following years.

I used the same process to locate bargains in a subdivision where each two-acre lot had been priced in the $8,000-10,000 range for several years. Suddenly, prices rose significantly. I purchased one site for $15,000 and another for $17,500, after making many phone calls and writing several letters to out-of-state owners. Within six months after purchase, the lots were worth at least $25,000 each.

Case Study:
Broker Contacts Can Yield Exceptional Prices

I followed an acre lot that was on my market-research data list for about eight years. At one time it was on the market at a high price. Several years later it sold for its true value. After a while, it came on the market again, but I was not immediately aware of it. Fortunately, I was acquainted with a successful real estate broker in the community, who called me with the news. Because the sellers were going through a bitter divorce, they were trying to harm each other by continually lowering the price. When the broker contacted me, the land was listed at only about 65 percent of its true value. I signed an offer at their asking price the next day.

Case Study:
Site Terrain Should Be Inspected Carefully

When I inspected a particular lot, I noticed that the rear two-thirds of the property sloped to a seasonal creek bed along the rear lot line. A neighbor remarked about the high cost of obtaining enough earth fill for grading his rear yard. Even the front one-third of the lot looked a bit low to a casual prospective buyer. I brought in my surveying instrument and discovered that the basement excavation would probably yield enough earth to fill the front yard. By leaving the rear yard wild, I could accomplish several things:

- The buyers of the home would have less grass to cut.
- I wouldn't have the cost of bringing in loads of fill.
- The wild trees to the rear of the proposed home would be an asset that earth filling would have destroyed.

After a little negotiation, I purchased this site for at least 10 percent below its true value.

Case Study:
Subsoil Problems Should be Discovered Early

A client chose a lot in a subdivision recently taken over by a large land developer. When the client consulted with me before signing an offer to purchase the lot, I advised her to stipulate that the seller warrant that subsoil conditions be adequate for the construction of an eleven-course concrete block basement and a six-course block attached garage foundation. The developer signed the agreement with these stipulations but neglected to probe the site prior to signing. Later, a test excavation revealed that original topsoil on this filled lot was several feet below proposed footing levels. The problem was solved by excavating wider and deeper than normal to reach original subsoil. Loads of large-diameter crushed rock were then brought in and compacted in layers up to the bottom of the normal footings.

Labor and expenses were entirely covered by the developer's labor crews, equipment, and materials. Had he not amended the contract, my client would have had to sell the site at a substantial loss, as she couldn't have absorbed the extra costs.

Later, I purchased a lot from the same developer. I was nearly ready to apply for a building permit when I visited the site on a day when the adjacent home was open. I noticed that a large corner of the basement floor was stepped up from the rest of the floor. According to the broker, a rock ledge had been uncovered during the basement excavation process. I suspected that the lot I was purchasing might have an even higher rock ledge problem. After some discussion, the developer agreed to drill and dynamite the site and the sewer/water hookup line location so that excavation and construction could proceed in a conventional fashion. My only expense was the extra grading time involved in dealing with the shattered limestone.

Had I completed the lot purchase before viewing the home next door, I would have been left with an expense that could have cut the gross profit by 50 percent.

Conducting an Overall Land Search

"Sometimes I only find out where I should be going by going somewhere I didn't want to be." — Buckminster Fuller

The case studies discussed in this chapter help to illustrate why shopping and market research must be constant, ongoing duties. Every community has desirable residential areas. Get into the habit of analyzing every community, including those visited on vacations. After a while, quick identification of desirable areas in any town will be second nature.

The following are the three most obvious sources of information for land research. They may be the only ones your competitors use.

• Sites discovered from your vehicle. Take alternate routes to regular destinations whenever possible. Something interesting might turn up.

- Building sites advertised in various newspapers—both the "For Sale by Owner" classifieds and the broker display ads.
- Most important is a relationship with one or two real estate brokers who know how to work with builders. Brokers are in the business to sell anything that will yield a commission; however, once in a while they'll uncover a particularly good deal for you. Ongoing contact is important.

The following is a checklist of other suggestions for identifying suitable sites or areas:

- Focus on locations where other builders are active. Determine the active areas for homes within your working price range.
- Look for land in an area that is increasing in value—this will make selling easier. On a metropolitan area map, draw some boundaries around these areas.
- Try to select areas that will be equally desirable in a year or two. Market research and your own instincts will be the guide in forecasting these "hot" locations.
- Obtain aerial photos whenever possible. They can reveal parcels that are not obvious from your vehicle. A large aerial photo will show each location's relationship with workplaces, shopping, schools, recreation, etc. The transportation links between them will also become apparent.
- Study county plat (ownership) books, which are available at libraries, map stores, or the county courthouse.
- Look at soil maps from the Department of Agriculture, which may help in avoiding areas that will probably fail a septic system percolation test or contain unstable foundation soils.
- Talk to surveyors about new subdivision locations and get overall advice on soils, terrain, and activity.
- In large metropolitan areas, consult with title companies. They sometimes provide monthly or quarterly newsletters about the activity in new subdivisions and new home sales.
- Read local newspapers for articles on various residential developments, along with real estate advertisements. But remember, the best buy is often not actively on the market.

One advantage of a focused land search is intimate knowledge of a few square miles. Knowing every available parcel or lot and something about the lot owners will produce big dividends over the years. Also keep this in mind: When contacting individual land owners as part of a land search, phone calls or face-to-face meetings are much more effective than letters.

Your overall survey of a large area may reveal smaller areas or whole towns that are underdeveloped. Builder beware! Perhaps zoning laws require outsized lots, or the school system is poor. These negative features may change for the better, but you never know. Let another builder test the market first.

Other sources for a wide-angle search include:
- Tax attorneys and accountants with land-owning clients
- Soil engineering firms with developer clients
- Appraisers of farm lands
- Chambers of Commerce, for information on trends and employment
- The freeway commission, for their plans for extensions and new access ramps
- The local gas and electric utility companies and the phone company, who have departments that study future growth
- Large homebuilding firms whose land inventory has become too large
- Excavation and foundation contractors working for builders, who may know of active locations
- The planning department of a city, town, or county, for information on the latest development and the preferred path of future growth
- Government offices, to inquire about parcels with ongoing tax arrearages and parcels taken for non-payment

Before researching too long in any general area, be sure to visit the zoning departments of the governing bodies that have jurisdiction. Can your home be built for the proposed market price niche anywhere in this area? A reference collection of zoning information for all target areas can be compiled from zoning maps and other materials. The building permit office can provide the local building code for that jurisdiction, reflecting differences in requirements between different communities and between inspectors' interpretations of the code. These differences affect construction cost, of course, so cost differences should be assessed when considering land prices later.

Finally, by placing a classified ad under "Real Estate Wanted" with some degree of regularity, you may turn up one or two good deals out of many bad ones over a long period of time. The ad should state the price range and general location. One example is shown in Figure 4.1.

A final note: As long as our country has the benefit of low-priced gasoline and increasingly fuel-efficient cars, homes will be purchased further away from central areas. Driving distances to jobs and conveniences will continue to become longer. Many people are willing to spend an extra $25 a week on fuel to save $5,000-$10,000 on the price of their lot. This is another factor to keep in mind during your research. Other trends that may accelerate decentralization are the increasing fragmentation of city centers, "telecommuting," and increasing numbers of self-employed workers.

Wanted to buy: Land for single family home. Western suburbs. Price range: $15–35K. Cash or terms. No brokers, please. Phone 555-1234 — leave message.

Figure 4.1 Sample Classified Advertisement

Narrowing the Land Search

Once you have conducted a wide-angle search, possible purchases will be apparent. At this point a more thorough analysis is appropriate. It is easy to become over-enthusiastic about a piece of land; this is one case in which the power of negative thinking is important. List all the reasons for *not* buying a specific parcel, as well as the reasons to buy. This is one way to remain aware of possible risks. Also determine whether the site has any liabilities that can be transformed into assets: for example, a low area that can be used for an attractive pond site instead of being filled.

In general, avoid lots on busy streets, most corner lots, and lots with incompatible neighbors. A low price is never enough compensation for a poor location. It's common to look at fifty or more lots before buying one.

The checklist in Figure 4.2 contains a number of criteria that can be used in selecting a site. The following sections describe other special considerations that might be part of your land evaluation process.

Privacy

Many homeowners value privacy quite highly. The supply of sites offering privacy is always short of the demand. An extra degree of privacy can sometimes be obtained in a subdivision setting where there is an oversized lot, existing vegetation, hills and berms, long setbacks from the road, or simply careful design of the home.

Proximity to New Construction

It is a good strategy to build near the activity of other builders, as long as they are selling fast and have sound reasons for their success. The activity of competitors will generate a heavy traffic of brokers and buyers. This will make the site "self-advertising." However, to attract attention, you'll have to add features that are not offered by nearby competitors.

Infill Locations

Infill sites (those in established or older neighborhoods) are overlooked by most builders. These neighborhoods can offer mature landscaping, ready infrastructure, nearby shopping services, and location-name recognition. The big builders can't afford to build on just one site, away from their large operations. The infill neighborhood should have some super features, like a park, lake, river, a view, or university, that make it an outstanding place to live. When building in an established neighborhood, be mindful of blending new construction with existing houses without over-improving the immediate neighborhood.

Infill land is often overpriced. The land value can be determined by the residual method: First determine the value of the homes nearby. Then add or subtract the costs to turn each home into something similar to the proposed home. From the average adjusted neighborhood value, deduct construction costs and gross profit to determine the maximum price to pay for the land.

Site Selection Checklist

The Site

Location _____

Subdivision name _____

Price _____

    Price history _____

    Lot resale profit possibility _____

Terms _____

Taxes _____

    Assessment _____

    History of tax hikes _____

Size _____

    Dimensions _____

    Configuration _____

Road jurisdiction _____

    Pavement _____

Topography _____

    Number of sites _____

    Soil type _____

    Subsurface rock _____

    Filled land? _____

    Views _____

Zoning _____

    Master planning and proposed changes _____

    Setbacks _____

    Variance needed? _____

Covenants _____

Vegetation _____

Demolition needed _____

    Tree removal _____

Water _____

    Impurities _____

    Tap fees _____

    Approvals _____

    Availability _____

Figure 4.2 Site Selection Checklist

Site Selection Checklist (cont'd)

Sewer _____

    Tap fees _____

    Septic approval and septic costs _____

    Sewerage pump _____

Telephone _____

Electric _____

Natural gas _____

Easements _____

Driveway possibilities _____

    Curb cuts _____

    Culverts _____

    Parking regulations _____

Nearby nuisances _____

Natural water courses _____

Attractions (water, views, neighbors, etc.) _____

Self-advertising location _____

Copy of plat _____

    Survey _____

Problems _____

    Floodplain _____

    Objectionable traffic _____

    Poor drainage _____

    Air pollution _____

    Unsightly views _____

    Noise _____

    Air traffic _____

    Forest fires _____

    Land/mud slides _____

    Earthquakes _____

    Multi-family, commercial, or industrial establishment
      in close proximity _____

General Area
    Quality of schools _____

    Environmental problems _____

    Tests and reports _____

Figure 4.2 Site Selection Checklist (cont'd)

Site Selection Checklist (cont'd)

Crime problems _____

Distance _____

    Driving _____

    Airport _____

    Road type to:

        Employment _____

        Shopping _____

            Entertainment/recreation _____

            Public transportation _____

    Building Permits _____

        Moratoriums _____

        Processing time _____

        Fees (impact or special) _____

        Possible fee increases _____

    Attitudes of lenders _____

        To community or subdivision _____

        To available utilities _____

Comments of builders' association, title company _____

Comments of engineer/surveyor _____

Comments of suppliers and subcontractors _____

Comments of appraiser _____

Comments of lenders _____

Advice of realtors _____

High-quality projects nearby (planned or existing) _____

Traffic created by other spec builders _____

Land use planning for the surrounding area (often overlooked) _____

Comparisons

With other offerings _____

Value-adding possibilities (subdivision, tree removal, cutting/filling) _____

Number and price of homes for sale nearby _____

Neighborhood home value range _____

Underbuilt or overbuilt _____

Figure 4.2 Site Selection Checklist (cont'd)

Undeveloped Land

In general, try to avoid undeveloped land requiring roads or water and sewer lines, especially if you are a novice spec builder. Many builders have been ruined by the very complex and risky business of developing land for home sites or by the carrying cost of a large inventory of developed lots. (Incidentally, these same builders can be a source of bargain lots.)

Land development is no place for amateurs. The risks are greater than in any other real estate venture. The subdividing of a parcel into a small number of lots, where roads and most utilities are already in place, should be the only land development attempted by a small builder.

Evaluating a Site

Before looking at a site, you'll need to do some homework. First confirm that zoning rules and subdivision covenants allow the proposed design, then drive out to see the land. Is the drive to the site pleasant or depressing? Are there any natural or man-made green belt areas nearby? These are becoming increasingly popular.

Take a Walk

Many people buy a piece of land without getting out of their car to set foot on it. It is important to walk the boundaries and the entire interior, studying trees, vegetation, terrain, rocks, views, and natural drainage, both around the house site and to and from neighboring sites. Listen for any disturbing sounds, such as loud traffic, industrial and commercial noises, wind speeds, barking dogs, airplane traffic, or construction noise. Also note any offensive agricultural or industrial odors.

Bring Some Tools

A 100-foot tape will help locate lot corners and determine where zoning setbacks and offsets define the area the home is to occupy. It is also helpful to remember the surveyor's rule of thumb that two steps equal five feet.

A simple hand-held telescope level has a bubble inside the viewing scope to show what objects are level with the eye. This will help determine if a sloping lot will require expensive earth fill or removal, if the home design will fit the site, or if there are drainage problems that can be corrected.

Another good tool is a camera to take photos of the land, the surroundings, and any special features.

Look Around

Neighboring construction that is underway can provide a glimpse of subsoil conditions. Some builders assume that for each foot that the land is too low, the cost of building or filling may increase at least $1,000. Sometimes enough earth fill is available from the basement, foundations, or septic system excavations.

If the land requires construction of a well to create a water supply, check with an active, reliable well driller as to the depth and productivity of neighboring wells. In addition, you can try dowsing or "well witching." Dowsing requires two stout pieces of wire (like a coat hanger), each about sixteen inches long with a bend at a right angle three inches from the end. The method is to hold the short ends between the thumb and forefinger of each hand, keeping the long ends level to the ground and parallel to each other (about twelve inches apart). The long portions of the wires should cross when passing significant water veins. It is helpful to practice walking over land with known water and sewer lines.

When using this technique on an unfamiliar piece of land, you should walk in both parallel and grid-like patterns to determine where underground streams run. There may be more than one source. The best location tends to be where two veins intersect.

Determining Value

Home-building industry consultants consistently find that a large portion of builders pay too much for land. First, consider the ratio of land cost to the ultimate package price. The land cost should be for ready-to-build land, including sewer and water service to the home as well as any cost attached to the roadway in front and a driveway opening or culvert. Is the land cost typical for the community? As stated in Chapter 2, a land cost that is 25 percent of the finished package price is common. For example, if the lot cost is $35,000: 35,000 x 4 = 140,000. Is a $140,000 home high or low compared to nearby homes? If it's too high, you'll need a lower lot price. If most nearby homes sell for $150,000–160,000, however, this may be a good opportunity. You can then build a home that will be priced up to $150,000 and offer more home size and quality per square foot while still competing with neighboring homes. These ratios can vary widely throughout the country.

Don't buy any piece of land until you have done a cost and gross profit feasibility analysis by using a cost breakdown sheet as a collection of known costs and best guesstimates.

Ascertaining Maximum Price for a Neighborhood

Consider the volatility of various components of this business. Land costs are the most volatile, rents the least volatile, and construction costs fall in the middle. One strategy for dealing with rapidly rising land costs is to purchase several lots at a time, but only if you can use the land in one or two years (unless you can resell some lots at a good profit without building on them). Land carried for speculative resale should be capable of appreciating at 20 percent per year. The historical average rate of appreciation in land prices is 5 percent to 7 percent annually.

A good formula for setting a limit on the maximum allowable price for a spec home, in order to avoid overimproving the neighborhood, is as follows: Gather enough value data about nearby homes to determine a price level at which 90 percent of surrounding homes (in up to a half-mile radius) are under the price and 10 percent are above it. Then add 15 percent to this price. If the resulting price doesn't fit the neighborhood, don't build here. A price of 15 percent to 20 percent above this "off center" value is the absolute upper limit a builder can allow a new product to upgrade a neighborhood.

A homogeneous neighborhood will usually have a 25 percent to 50 percent maximum spread of values. For example, the least expensive home might be $100,000, while the most expensive is $125,000 or $150,000. In a less homogeneous area, where the value might range from $60,000 to $180,000, for example, a new product should be targeted to the lower half of the range. Scattered sites that are not in a subdivision are often examples of non-homogeneous neighborhoods. You'll need some extra analysis in these areas.

If there is an agreeable lot in an area where the typical 2,000-square-foot home sells for less than anywhere else in the metropolitan area, you should be suspicious. Local buyers' financial abilities may be weak, or competing builders may be very efficient.

While considering the neighboring homes around a potential lot, remember that the immediately adjacent homes have much more effect on a home's value than more distant lots.

A helpful exercise is to consider both the lowest-priced home and the highest-priced home that could sell on a particular site, and analyze each one to compare gross profit margins. It's possible to realize the same profit margin with less money at risk in a smaller, lower-priced home.

Case Study:
Trees and Other Variables Can Affect Site Value

Land with trees, except in very heavily wooded regions, has a higher value than land without trees. Trees can add 7 percent to the value of the finished product. In a mountain suburb, I discovered that a two-acre lot with an adequate number of trees was worth about 20 percent more than an equivalent lot without any trees. If the lot sloped enough to present some real driveway difficulties, it was worth 15 to 20 percent less. If the lot had a view, it was worth at least 10 percent more than one with no view. If the view was terrific, it was worth at least 20 percent more.

Considering Lot Variations

Lot size variations often confuse land buyers. The tendency is to think of land values in terms of so many dollars per acre. In an area zoned for one-acre minimum lot sizes, a one-and-one-half-acre lot is not worth 50 percent more. Each acre represents one legal building site, so a one-and-one-half-acre parcel still represents only one building site; the ability to build is what gives the land most of its value. However, this "excess land" (over the legal minimum) does have some value. This value is usually at about 60 percent of the prorated value per square foot or per acre of the minimum lot size required by zoning or covenants. A two-acre site that can be legally divided is worth 100 percent more after division costs are accounted for.

When considering smaller city-sized lots, a lot with only 50 percent of the average depth may have a value equal to 70 percent of a normal lot. A lot with 150 percent of the average depth may have a value of 120 percent of the normal lot. To become more familiar with variations in lot values, refer to a good textbook on real estate appraisal, and monitor a local community by keeping a list of land and lot values. Your local market may vary from the examples provided here and from generic textbook formulas.

For lots served by a sewer line, the sewer should be low enough to allow for the lateral line from the proposed home to drain into it. Sometimes a slight variation in the slope of the service lateral can be constructed—you can discuss this with the local municipal engineer. If the site requires a sewerage lift pump and grinder, avoid it. It will turn off a buyer who can easily purchase another home without this unusual device. Be sure to confirm easy hook-up to other services, including water service or a well, electric, cable TV, and telephone (for example, the site may be just beyond metropolitan phone service).

Some lot problems are correctable, as illustrated in the case studies presented earlier in this chapter. Environmental hazards—for example, land that was part of a former landfill—can be lethal to your business. There are companies that provide data on environmental reports nationwide. They can give information on a lot with just an address or legal description.

You may need a zoning variance to solve a building-footprint infringement problem in an odd-shaped lot. The granting of the variance should be made a contingency for the lot purchase. Try to avoid land that requires a complete zoning change. Other contingencies for purchase of land are covered in the next section.

While most subdivision covenants actually do protect values and desirability, you might run across a requirement that reduces the number of buyers for your product. One example is jokingly called the "fat dog" clause: "No homeowner shall keep a dog that weighs over 20 pounds."

Going Forward with the Offer to Purchase

Once you have completed your research and selected a site, you will probably be anxious to get to the next step: the offer to purchase the land. The first issue to deal with, of course, is the price of the lot.

Negotiating Price

Purchasing a lot of land for the lowest possible price relies heavily on good negotiating skills. There are several good books and tapes available about the general negotiation process (see the Resources Appendix).

Research should reveal the true value of the site. Twenty percent off the asking price may be a good starting offer, but if the offer is much too low, the seller may be insulted and assume a defensive posture. Or the seller may not take the offer seriously.

If you have a broker's license, you may be able to purchase at a discount, thereby reducing the price by at least half of the commission amount. Often land developer discounts are given to any established builder, based on the possibility of repeat business.

The cash balance at an early closing may help you to buy at the lowest price, but small builders in some states use subdivider subordinated financing. This involves the seller receiving most and sometimes all of the sale proceeds in the form of a promissory note that is not recorded until after the builder obtains the construction loan. The land purchase loan then becomes subordinated to the primary construction loan/mortgage/first deed of trust. Should the builder fail to repay the loan, the construction loan would be paid from the proceeds of a foreclosure sale; the remaining sale proceeds, if any, would be applied to this second note/mortgage/deed of trust. Any developer willing to hold subordinated paper should be glad to offer a good discount for a cash sale.

Using Contingencies

In a land purchase offer/contract, there are many ways for you to protect yourself from costly problems. The importance of contingencies in a land purchase contract cannot be overemphasized. Care in covering all the risks will reduce unexpected costs and delays. Some possible contingencies are listed below.

Architectural Approval

The sale can be contingent upon architectural approval of home plans by whoever has the power (the subdivider, subdivision committee, or municipal architectural board). In this case, it is best to have a set of plans ready so approval, rejection, or further negotiations can take place prior to the closing date. With plans in hand and the house location determined, it's possible to cross this hurdle right after offer/contract time.

Issuance of Building Permit

The sale can be contingent upon the issuance of a building permit. This could be critical in case of a permit moratorium. The only risks will be time and costs in preparing plans and site survey work for permit payment and issuance before closing.

Septic System Approval

The sale can be contingent upon receipt of county or state approval for a standard conventional septic system without a pump. Then if the approved system involves an expensive extra tank and pump, or is not a conventional system, you have the option to back out of the land purchase or negotiate a lower price with the seller.

Soil Inspection

The sale can be contingent upon inspection of proposed foundation soil bearing capacity or rock excavation problems. Subsoil experiences were related in the case studies earlier in this chapter.

Construction Loan

The sale can be contingent upon the buyer obtaining a construction loan for a spec home. Be sure to use this contingency if you have no other source of funds and you are not absolutely sure you will be able to obtain a construction loan.

Miscellaneous

The sale can be contingent upon certain items such as:

- Issuance of a well permit
- Hook-up approval for local water or sewer system
- Granting of a zoning variance for infringing upon the zoning ordinance side yard, rear yard, or setback requirements
- Survey work to determine the exact parcel and the size planned for
- Any other potential problem that could affect the land, house plan, or construction schedule.

You may not want to purchase a site where construction cannot start on schedule because the developer has not received his governmental "ready for home construction permits" or subdivision/development approvals in a timely fashion.

Expenses

Be prepared to pay for all tests, permits, and surveys necessary to cover contingencies. Also allow adequate time before the closing date for full execution. You may have to turn all surveys and test results over to the seller as partial compensation when it's necessary to back out of the purchase. The costs of these protective tests should not be prohibitive—most of them will be needed later anyway.

For additional protection and as a negotiating item, be willing to pay several hundred nonrefundable dollars to have the seller extend the time for clearing up any contingency for another 30 days. Perhaps you can arrange for the seller to apply these extra dollars to the purchase price balance if contingencies are satisfied before the expiration time.

Using Options

Options are widely used by larger builders to tie up the land they need later, and to avoid possible price increases. When a builder asks a seller (via the option) to withhold a parcel of land from sale to other parties for a period of time (with no guarantee of purchase), the seller may want interest payments and other carrying costs covered by the price of the option. Options can generally be obtained for half of the carrying costs.

The option expiration period may be for any length of time that is mutually agreeable. When feasible, try to negotiate for the option's cost to be applied to the purchase price. During a shortage of building sites or a period of rising site costs, options offer a way to hold down lot costs without freezing capital.

An interesting form of option is the rolling option. Here the purchaser has options for the purchase of several lots. The exercise time period is generally somewhat flexible. For example, the purchaser must buy one lot every three months to keep the option alive. If the purchaser falls behind the three-month schedule, the option to purchase the remaining lots is lost. A small builder might purchase just one or two lots for cash and option one or two more lots for six months later. In this case the option may be offered at a very nominal price considering the concurrent cash purchase of one or two lots.

It is wise to use an attorney for drafting land purchase documents. Eventually you may develop enough skill and knowledge to draft your own documents, but a thorough real estate background is needed for this important contract document. The use of attorneys is covered in more detail in Chapter 10.

It isn't advisable to make a large deposit with an offer—2 percent to 5 percent should be enough. Get the master title policy number, if there is one, for the subdivision. Consult your local title company.

Advancing the Ground-Breaking Date

After completing the purchase contract, receiving a satisfactory title insurance commitment, and confirming that any contingencies will be satisfied and no other problems with the lot purchase will arise, it may be safe to commence construction before the actual closing on the lot purchase. In most instances a lender will not allow this for prior lien and loan security reasons, but if you are financing construction with personal funds or loans that rely on other property or securities as collateral, you may be able to shorten the overall time span between contract for purchase and completion of the home. This can be a great help in finishing the rough construction that could be delayed by the onset of bad weather. You might go so far as to obtain the survey work and building permit, excavate, complete foundation work, and backfill earth around the foundation in the period between purchase contract/title evidence and the closing of the land purchase.

Summary

A good deal of information has been presented in this chapter. The importance of careful land selection is illustrated by the overwhelming number and variety of factors to be considered in the selection process.

After the lot has been selected, the next important factor to be considered is the actual design of the home to be built. Chapter 5 discusses this process in detail.

Key Points
- The most obvious sources of information for land research are sites discovered from your vehicle; sites advertised in newspapers; and real estate brokers. Other sources include aerial photos, soil maps, and title companies.
- Determine all the reasons for *not* buying a specific lot as well as the reasons to buy.
- Build near the activity of other builders, as long as they are selling fast and have sound reasons for their success.
- Infill locations can offer mature landscaping, ready infrastructure, nearby shopping, and location-name recognition, but be careful about going over the neighborhood value level.
- Avoid undeveloped land requiring roads or water and sewer lines.
- Determine a price level at which 90 percent of area homes are under the price and 10 percent are above it; then add 15-20 percent to the price. If the resulting price doesn't fit the neighborhood, don't build there.
- Some lot problems are correctable, but environmental hazards can be lethal to your business.
- Contingencies in a land purchase contract can include architectural approval of home plans; issuance of a building permit; septic system approval; and soil inspection.
- Be prepared to pay for all tests, permits, and surveys necessary to cover contingencies.
- Options are widely used by larger builders to tie up the land they need later and to avoid possible price increases. Try to apply the option's cost to the purchase price.

Chapter 5
Design Decisions & Value Engineering

The Cost and Value of Good Design

Both first-time spec builders and "laypeople" who are designing their own homes sometimes use old plans that have not been popular for many years and that may never regain popularity. The exteriors and floor plans are reminiscent of homes of decades past, especially in ranch/rambler or tri-level designs. The result is a brand new home that appears 30 years old.

The first home I designed and built for myself was based solely on personal desires and tastes. After construction, I realized the errors. On my first spec home, I incorporated ideas from an efficient and attractive home designed by a large local builder. These ideas improved my original design to a great extent.

The widespread practice of exactly duplicating existing home plans, however, is unethical. Many established builders' plans have been copied by others — usually without permission. With recent legislation, this practice is now legally dangerous. It is wise to remain cautious in this area, especially if your proposed design is almost an exact copy of another builder's plans.

I have recently been involved as a plaintiff in copyright lawsuits for 10 buildings using my design without my permission. Out-of-court settlements were equal to about 3% of the value of the finished product. Court settlements as high as 15% of finished product value are on record.

From the 1960s to the 1980s, skilled home designers charged about 50¢/S.F. of living area to design and draft a set of home plans. Perhaps it is close to $1/S.F. now. In the Midwest, local builders are paying $500 - $1500 or more for 2,200-square-foot home plans. This cost varies depending on the region. These plans can be well-drafted and targeted to the local market but for this price, the designer usually cannot afford to examine all options to increase final value or lower initial costs.

Large home-building firms that employ professional architects and design staffs often spend a full year developing a new model home. Some firms report costs of $50,000 or more to develop a new home design. This amount of time and resources ensures an attractive design with carefully engineered construction costs; and in large firms these high design costs can be prorated over hundreds of homes. If you're a small builder you can't afford this approach, but by carefully studying these homes, you can learn some important cost and design concepts.

Idea Sources

When searching for detail or design concepts, study homes built by successful firms whose models satisfy the local market. As I have already mentioned, other builders are a great source of market research and design ideas. Stay informed by keeping abreast of local newspapers, brokers' opinions, and buyers' comments. With experience and research, again, you can learn to spot good design in any location. Good architectural design, like good art, can be difficult to explain; it must be experienced firsthand.

Save copies of good plans. Develop a file catalog of details (bath ideas, kitchen layouts, fireplace details, etc.). Analyze the comparative costs of designs by comparing exterior total wall surface areas to enclosed living space. Get involved in the preliminary sketch- and scale-drawing process, even if working drawings are completed by a hired designer or draftsperson. Notice large building firms' use of many comprehensive detailed drawings in the working plans. Imagine the cost savings in material purchases, labor, and supervision.

Often small builders or new builders purchase working plans by mail. The price of "stock plans" is low and they are designed for a wide range of users, not primarily for the purpose of building and selling speculative homes. Changes generally need to be made to these drawings to adapt them to the local market, local building codes, and site conditions. Furthermore, the features of stock plans must be carefully evaluated to determine which are appropriate and economical for a successful spec home. I sometimes refer to stock plans for ideas and save certain pages of builder magazine plans for my files. Builders should be very selective in their choice of stock plans and plan companies.

In short, do a very thorough job to produce a design that can offer the buyer an attractive house for the price. Remember, this plan, or revisions of it, may be repeated many times.

Bibliographical Resources

There are a great many books on the subjects of general architecture and home design. The Resources Appendix includes an annotated listing of books on these and other topics that are basic to your development as a spec builder.

Architects and Designers

Not everyone understands the difference between the occupations of designer and architect. An architect's background includes extensive education and work experience, which are necessary before taking a lengthy examination administered by a state licensing board. In most states, a residential designer is usually not required to be tested and licensed. A designer is limited to executing plans for one- or two-family dwellings. Three-family dwellings and larger apartment/condominium buildings usually require state approval of plans drafted by a licensed architect or engineer.

While skilled in design, many architects are not closely aware of construction costs and not all are acutely attentive to public reaction to their work. Some residential designers are quite talented and can produce work that is closely in tune with prevailing trends. However, when the work of an architect who specializes in home design is compared with that of a good unlicensed designer, the architect's work is usually superior.

Costs for Services

The price of an architect's services is about two to four times the cost of a designer's services. I have hired architects on an hourly basis for suggestions and elevation solutions and found it worthwhile. Be sure to use the services of an architect or designer who is experienced in designing homes of a similar size and type to the one you are building. Many well-established designers and some architects have developed portfolios of house plans that are available for reproduction or revision and can be purchased at very reasonable cost, compared with starting from scratch. Often they have done work for larger, successful builders, so check out their portfolios.

The cost of preliminary sketches and design work is about one-third the total beginning-design-to-working-drawing cost. Some builders do their own preliminaries and hire out the remaining work, thereby maximizing the communication of their ideas while saving one-third of the total design cost. Preliminary sketches and working drawings are discussed further later in this chapter.

Engineers

You may need to consult with a structural engineer for a framing or foundation problem. For foundation and soil work, be sure to hire a well-experienced specialist who also provides soil boring tests for foundations. Rarely will you need to hire an engineer for a framing problem. If you are building spec homes for a living, you should have an understanding of loads (both distributed and concentrated), dead loads, live loads, spans, cantilevers, fiber stress, modulus of elasticity, and related simple calculations. You may be able to find a less expensive solution to a beam span problem, for example, if you are aware of several options.

The staff at your lumber dealer, truss manufacturer, or structural steel supplier can provide all the structural engineering assistance you will need in most cases. If you must hire a licensed structural engineer, be ready for a little "engineering overkill," as these engineers must be extremely thorough to avoid any possibility of liability.

Doing It Yourself

When acting as designer and draftsperson, be aware of potential pitfalls and personal limitations. Don't be afraid to ask for opinions. I once asked a framing carpenter if he thought the roof pitch on my one-and-one-half story home under construction should have been a 12/12 instead of the 10/12 that was used. He thought the 12/12 pitch would have caused the house to appear top-heavy. When I experimented with the idea at my drawing board, I saw that he was correct.

Figure 5.1 shows a simple floor plan and sketch of a home design built many times by my company. It is no longer being built because furniture arrangement in the family room was difficult, and because currently a design with the family room separated from the living room is preferred by most buyers in this home size and price market. This design, however, was successful for a number of years in the move-up market in which it was built. It was the highest-value, lowest-price home that my company designed and built. The qualities that made the plan successful were three "extra" features: a fourth bedroom, a whirlpool tub, and garage space for a third car. None of these features was being offered by the competition in this price range. Value engineering applied to house shape, floor space, and material selection allowed me to hold the price down, yet offer a locally-popular floor plan and exterior style. Over a period of time, I discovered that the third-car garage space was the most highly valued of the "extras."

Professional Builder and the National Association of Home Builders (NAHB) offer a service to help builders solve floor plan problems and discover new ideas. Free of charge, the NAHB Design Committee will review your floor plan and suggest alternatives to improve its "livability and salability." You must provide a blueprint of the plan, a description of your target market, and a cover note (*Professional Builder*, August 1994). See the Resources Appendix for the address to take advantage of this service.

The real test of any design comes after the actual construction. Designers who also build and then live in their designs become better designers.

The Importance of Market Research

We discussed market research in Chapter 3; it is important enough to mention again. The design stage is the time when market research is applied. One way to add value to a spec home is to cater to the local preferences and trends. Have your favorite realtor comment on your plans.

A spec home design should strive to incorporate features that have local acceptance but have not been widely offered by the competition in new or existing homes. These features should be included if their inclusion still allows you to compete at a price near that of similar-sized new homes. The design amenities should place it between the tract home and the custom home—the closer to a custom look, the better.

The exterior design must fit into the neighborhood without being a replica of a nearby home. Be careful not to over-improve the neighborhood: Most of the prospects looking in the area won't be able to afford an over-improved house, and those who can afford it will want to live in a higher-priced neighborhood.

Try to be aware of design trends. For example, currently master bedrooms tend to be very large. Home offices in a spare den or bedroom are popular. A gas line to the fireplace is also important. Also, although buyers always ask about the total floor space in the home, the *perception* of space is equally important. Good architecture is the creation of illusions. If a home appears 10 to 15 percent larger than it is, it is a competitive and profitable product.

The Highlander

Featuring four bedrooms, two and one-half baths, whirlpool tub and three-car garage.

About this home

During the past twenty years, we have designed and built a variety of homes. The **Highlander** offers great value in a four bedroom home with a three car garage.

Many of the features found in the **Highlander** are usually found in larger or more expensive homes. Window placement and floor plan combine to create a light and spacious atmosphere.

Through extensive on-site supervision and by limiting the number of homes we build each year, we can control the quality of your new home and its timely completion.

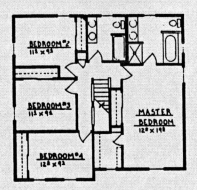

Features

- Almost 2100 sq. ft. Expandable options to 2400 sq. ft.
- Reinforced poured concrete basement with insulation below grade.
- Oak doors, cabinets, trim, and custom oak fireplace mantle and surround.
- Washable, off-white drywall painting included.
- 200 amp. electrical service
- 50 gallon water heater.
- Cedar siding.

Base Price $ _____

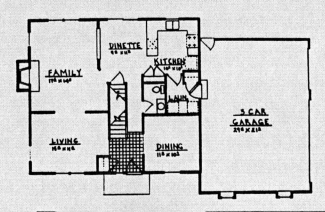

RIDGELINE
HOMES

design
construction
real estate

For more information contact:

Ken Johnson

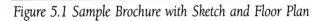

Figure 5.1 Sample Brochure with Sketch and Floor Plan

Finally, if your market research indicates that a good portion of your prospective buyers are now apartment dwellers, realize that they will be very interested in closet storage space, kitchen storage, and kitchen counter space.

General Design Criteria

As discussed in Chapter 1, a good floor plan is an essential key to the success of a spec home. When designing a home, give the floor plan high priority. Strive for a balance between being innovative and being conventional. Go over the room types, sizes, locations, and the linkages between them very thoroughly. Bring in natural light in as many ways as possible. Try to satisfy the market by providing *perceived* space and elegance with a minimum of overall floor space and exterior wall surface. Elegant home designs require being aware of proportions. A short study of the "golden mean" will help you to understand this (see *Experiencing Architecture* by Rasmussen, listed in the Resources Appendix). Even the simplest home design can be elegant. Also, if you have a large site, a wide home/garage will appear to "lay claim" to the land.

The exterior style of the building could be transitional, somewhere between traditional and contemporary. If a transitional design is acceptable in your market, it may attract both contemporary- and traditional-minded buyers.

In general, avoid plans that are difficult to build; that require long, skillful hours to frame; and that use framing materials in excess. When you present plans like these to subcontractors, you will probably receive high bids. You can reach your goals with a design that is as simple as a cube with a short one- or two-story bay and extra gable attached to the front. Of course, it must still look elegant and well proportioned.

Your Design "Program"

Before beginning any design sketches, write a list of objectives—your design "program." Avoid your own personal desires; don't allow your ego to get in the way. Figure 5.2 is an example of a typical design program for a home built during the 1980s.

Exterior Atmosphere: Orientation and Curb Appeal

Many buyers are not aware of the importance of orientation until after they move in. It is important to emphasize this attribute during the sales process. Educating prospective buyers about such aspects as a well-positioned home can mean faster sales.

Sunlight: A Source of Warmth and Interior Atmosphere

Too many of today's new homes are built with no regard for the movement of the sun and its effect both on the home's occupants and on heating and cooling costs. Even in the coldest climates, it is common to see homes with garages attached to the south side of the home, allowing no house windows to bring in winter warmth and brightness. Dinettes are sometimes located on the cold north elevation. Floor plans often don't fit sites, and entire end walls of two-story homes may have no windows at all. In designing and building spec homes, try to plan for the effects of sunlight.

Type	Two-story home for economy of construction and market satisfaction.
Size	1,800–2,200 square feet with 1,000 square feet on first floor, per zoning.
Exterior	Traditional, to fit into the subdivision.
Foyer/Entry	Roofed entry porch; vaulted foyer ceiling. Kitchen/dinette not visible from entry door.
Great Room	Fireplace; 13-1/2 feet minimum room width; 250 square feet minimum overall size; beam ceiling.
Formal Dining Room	Near kitchen; may flow from great room if space is defined with arch or half-wall wings; optional crown molding.
Kitchen/Dinette	275 square feet minimum; U-shaped counter layout; planning desk; microwave oven cabinet; large pantry.
First-Floor Den	Off foyer is best, but near garage entry is acceptable; 110–140 square feet; small closet; optional hardwood floor and double door.
First-Floor Laundry	Near garage entry and kitchen, not in kitchen; cabinet laundry tub and lower-priced wall cabinets.
Garage	At least 22' x 22'; overhead door faces side yard, if possible.
Garage-to-House Entry	Not into a room — into a hallway; with a jacket closet organized for hats, gloves, and boots.
Second Floor	Three bedrooms; two baths.
Hall Bath	Fiberglass tub and shower; 36″ minimum vanity width.
Master Bath	Fiberglass 48″ shower stall; 36″ minimum vanity out of bath; close to dressing area and walk-in closet.
Master Bedroom	Separated from the other bedrooms; 11' minimum width; 175 square feet minimum size (200 square feet is better), not including a dressing alcove.
Other Bedrooms	110–140 square feet each; large closets.
Overall	General look of affluence. Many buyers in this suburb want to display their success or newly acquired good fortune. Even though they cannot afford a 3,000 square foot home, it should have much the same effect.

Figure 5.2 Sample Design Program for a Spec Home

What rooms should receive bright sunlight? This decision requires some thought as to where various activities might take place, and at what times of the day they are likely to occur. Many people enjoy having breakfast in a bright, east-facing kitchen/dinette. On the other hand, my family did not enjoy eating supper with the hot sun glaring across the table on the west side of our first home. Most people spend a lot of time in their family or great rooms. Will they receive direct sunlight here, and is there a pleasant view from this room?

Before purchasing a site, imagine a proposed floor plan there. How will the sunlight come into certain rooms? Can the house be rotated slightly to take advantage of views and sunlight? If there is an attached garage in the plan, try to place it on the side of the home that faces cold, strong winds or unpleasant sounds or views.

Savings on heating costs are realized when a home is protected from cold winds and the winter sun enters rooms directly. For example, in one of our homes, 45 percent of all the window glass faced directly south. Our forced-air furnace did not operate between 10 a.m. and 3 p.m. on sunny days when the temperature outside was above 15°F.

Curb Appeal

Will your design appeal to a prospective buyer who is driving or walking by? Curb appeal is very important and will act as a "silent salesperson." Does the home offer perceived value? Will it appear as an unexpected delight to the buyer who has looked at dozens of other offerings? Does it appear to be a warm, welcoming yet elegant, tasteful home? The view from the curb should make any buyer anxious to see the interior; the stroll to the front entry should heighten these feelings.

Lines and Angles

A strong, interesting front elevation will enhance curb appeal. The strongest lines are the ground line, the eave line, the gables and overhangs, and the roof ridge lines. Strong horizontal lines can make a home appear larger. The roof angle and its color and texture are also important. The home may appear as a mass of blended, intersecting cubes and shapes, rather than just a box. I often see an unbroken roof eave line over both house and garage. In a case like this, bringing the garage forward a few feet could place a pleasant 8"–12" drop into the long horizontal line.

Siding

The exterior surfaces of the home also need a little variety; but no more than two types of wall surfaces (siding, brick, etc.) should be used. One material should be dominant. In general, use refined materials with the same general characteristics: for example, rustic horizontal siding, or rustic vertical siding, with rustic brick or stone. It's not a good idea to place slick smooth siding next to rough stone veneer.

Real wood siding, often beveled rough cedar, is highly valued in many parts of the country. Because of a depletion of good trees, however, the quality has been decreasing — there are usually too many knots and short lengths. I prefer a manufactured horizontal siding made of oriented strand board with a rough primed face stamped on it. It is very durable, inexpensive, weathertight, and easy to install and paint. I think it looks great; and most people assume it is real cedar.

In many markets, brickwork is highly regarded. Brick can easily cost four to five times more than siding, so use it sparingly and in the most effective places. Placing it on an outside fireplace chimney may not be the best choice. I prefer to use it across the width of the front porch, from porch floor to ceiling, and end at the protruding, sided bays or garage. It looks "cheap" to end the brick at an outside corner of the home. A brick veneer that reaches only to the first-floor window sills also looks outdated or out of balance.

Roofs

Main roof pitches shouldn't be too flat for one- and two-story homes. Avoid 4/12 pitches — 5 or 6 should be the minimum. I built many 4/12 roofs early in my career and was amazed to see what a difference a slightly steeper roof made in the overall appearance of homes built later.

Case Study:
Roof Pitch Variations Affect Overhangs

The pitch of the roof, the style of the home, and the local market will dictate the amount of roof overhang that is appropriate for a home. For years, I used a 24″ overhang on a two-story roof of 4 to 4-1/2 /12 pitch. When I used a 5-1/2 /12 or greater pitch, I cut the overhang back to 12 inches — the same dimension as the gable end roof overhang. No one noticed the change. I saved money on trusses, roof sheathing, roofing, and soffit materials. A beautifully shaped roof will add considerable curb appeal to any design.

Gables

At least one gable facing the street will add value and appeal. The gable could be placed over a garage, dormer, or protruding bay. It should be functional, not just ornamental. Front-facing gables often need to be of a steeper pitch than the main roof. When the bottoms of two gables that are at right angles meet, the roof surface of the smaller gable can be extended to two feet beyond the inside of the large rake to create an interlocking, well-constructed appearance.

A circular or semicircular gable vent, made of durable fiberglass, can help to accent a bland elevation.

Porches

Front entry porches are popular again. To design a well-proportioned and substantial porch, use square columns that are seven to nine inches thick (built-up or hollow) and set the railing balusters two to three inches apart.

Windows

Whenever possible, align the windows over each other for overall balance. In addition, try to minimize the variety of window sizes in the overall plan. Windows in the garage that are visible from the street should be similar in size and type to those used in the house.

There are several ways to improve the exterior appearance of windows, depending on the style of the home. Extra-wide, factory-applied casing boards are nice, but expensive. Job-applied add-on casings invite rainwater. A shop-made or site-made wood window crown works best. Flower pot sills or window boxes provide a nice accent under a large front window and have the same effect that foundation shrubbery will provide later. I like to use divided light grilles in the upper sash of street-facing, double-hung windows, and sometimes in all the windows. Omitting the grilles from the lower sashes not only cuts the grille cost in half, but also reflects a popular Victorian window style and provides an unobstructed view for people who are seated inside the house.

To promote an elegant and classic appearance, use windows that are tall rather than short and wide. You could use slightly shorter windows on the second floor. For double-hung windows, I use 28"-high glass in the sashes for the first floor and 24" high for the second floor. Casement windows look better on a rustic- or contemporary-style house. An angle bay window is great, but often a much less expensive box bay—with an 8" to 10" projection, a small shed roof over the exterior, and a wood or carpet interior seat/shelf—will do the job.

An octagon or round window can often improve a front elevation while illuminating a powder room, walk-in closet, foyer, or laundry.

Case Study:
Considering the Natural Landscape When Placing the House

The principles of landscape architecture are helpful in placing a home and in choosing an overall exterior appearance. A two-acre site I purchased in a mountainous area sloped steeply down from the road. As a result, the driveway had to be laid out in a switch-back route. The best house site was farther down the driveway, but a one-story home would have looked lost. A steep cedar shake roof on a one-and-one-half story home was the answer, allowing for a distant view over the treetops from the upper-level windows.

On a large site with a hilltop, consider placing the home slightly below the top, so it appears to hug the earth.

Interior Atmosphere: Again, the Importance of Light

Let's walk through a well-designed, two-story home.

Upon entering the home, there is a feeling of drama and surprise created by a two-story foyer. The foyer is also enhanced by stair railing balusters to the second floor. A balcony railing or half-wall on the second-floor hallway adds to the visual space. A fan light door adds sophistication. The "sightlines" from the foyer include a view across the house to sliding glass doors, through which we can see several trees. This view enhances the light, airy atmosphere that is evident throughout the house. The foyer floor is tile, but it could easily be brick, hardwood, or even premium sheet vinyl. In any event, the foyer—and the entire first floor—makes a high-quality impression.

The kitchen receives more natural light than any other room in the house. A window over the sink makes the work area bright and cheerful. The kitchen includes an adequate number of attractive wood cabinets with good-quality hardware, a stud and sheetrock pantry, generous counter space, overhead lighting, and an island counter. Standing in the kitchen, it is easy to see and converse with people in the adjacent dinette and the family room. It is a natural gathering area.

Windows are on as many walls as practical—especially near adjacent walls in a room. The light from one window overlapping the light from another window on a perpendicular wall creates a quality of light that is hard to duplicate in any other way. For a good explanation of the term "quality of light," read Chapter 6, "Daylight in Architecture," in Rasmussen's book, *Experiencing Architecture* (see the Resources Appendix). As you proceed through the rest of the house, you are drawn into each room by the light and view through the first window you see as you walk into the room. A window at the end of the hallway from a bedroom or bath overlooks the garage roof. Although the main second-floor bath affords no opportunity for a window, the small ceiling skylight makes it appear larger than it is. Throughout the house, there is never a feeling of enclosure or cramped spaces.

The fireplace location in the living room is such that you can envision a pair of sofas facing each other in front of it. The buyer may not ever furnish the room that way, but it is a common scenario seen on TV and in magazines.

A wide opening between the living room and formal dining room is upgraded and highlighted with a wood jamb, extra-wide casings, and a crown-type head casing—an upscale touch for little money in an eye-catching location.

The relationships and linkages between rooms is sensible and efficient. Parts of the home offer adequate individual privacy in contrast to the community possibilities of the gathering areas.

A Final Note on Windows

Don't assume that your total window cost needs to be over budget to accomplish your goal of natural lighting, or that a home with many windows will be too costly to heat. Adding just one or two extra windows, and placing every window in the right place, will do the trick. The atmosphere created by the well-planned introduction of natural light can easily set your house apart from the competition. Check the exterior elevation for a sense of balance.

Too many homes built today are not windowed properly. Visit the interiors of some 75- or 100-year-old houses and notice what those designers did with windows. You may hear that someone prefers a short window where chairs or a sofa may be placed against it; but light diffuses from a tall window around furniture and into the room. Taller windows look elegant from both the inside and the outside of a house.

The Importance of Color

Several academic studies have proven the importance of color. In architecture, color has more of an effect (positive or negative) than form or shape. Proper color selection greatly enhances overall architectural line and form. The best color cannot save a bad design, however. Likewise, poor color choices can destroy a fine design.

Exterior Colors

When confronted with difficult color choices, it is wise to err on the side of caution. The demographics of the local market need to be given consideration. Younger buyers are more apt to prefer more trendy colors, while older buyers lean toward traditional color choices. Be sure to use exterior colors that fit the architectural style of the house.

You will usually have to decide on a roof color early in the building process. Rather than selecting roofing colors from manufacturers' samples, observe roofs on existing homes. Roofing suppliers can furnish addresses of homes that have incorporated their materials. To select a roof color, narrow the siding or brick colors down to a few options. The selection of the wrong roof color will severely limit color options on the exterior of the building, so try to select all of the exterior colors at the same time.

For a home design that will be used more than once, plan two or three color combinations for the exterior that will look good and have widespread market acceptance. To make a small home appear larger, white siding and white trim work well with autumn brown roofing. Using white trim can save further painting of white factory-enameled storm doors, rain gutters, and storm sashes. If almost all the exterior colors are neutral, painting the entry door in a strong contrasting color can make a powerful statement.

Here are some rules of thumb for choosing exterior colors:
- For the body of the house, warm colors are inviting.
- A light color or lighter tone of the main body color can be used to accent detailed trim.
- When using light colors on the siding, thick siding butts help emphasize shadow lines.

When necessary, seek the advice of a professional decorator or consultant. Why ruin a good exterior design with colors that turn off prospects?

Interior Colors

The general goal of an interior color scheme is to enlarge the space with continuous, light colors. When using tile in a bath, use one color throughout. In the spec homes that I have built, all walls and ceilings are sprayed by the drywall contractor with a washable off-white paint. Another good drywall color is "twine," a very light hint of tan. It is a warm color that blends with most wood stains.

Doors, windows, and trim are usually stained to match prefinished cabinets in kitchens and bathrooms. Recently the trend has been to lighter cabinet and trim colors, but if there is a great variety of wood species, lighter tones can be a problem. Darker stains seem to minimize differences in wood grains and colors. There is no real formula for making a choice between light and dark stain. Although darker stains mask the irregularity in different wood types, you — and your market — may still prefer a lighter stain. Check with a builder's color consultant and talk with prospective buyers and brokers. At a certain point, you will have to rely on your own instincts.

Vinyl floor coverings should be neutral enough to blend with most furnishings without being too bland. Brickwork on the fireplace and ceramic tile on floors should look like brick and tile, as opposed to plastic or concrete. In general, it's best to stay with traditional, time-tested colors.

Carpeting is almost always selected by the buyer. One color or tone throughout is best—for example, avoid using brown in the hallway, blue in one bedroom, and rose in another. Encourage the buyer to choose neutral carpet colors, which are preferred by 75 percent of women buyers according to a nationwide survey. The home will look better to future prospects; and, should the buyer be unable to close because of an unexpected turn of events, neutral colors will be most attractive to other prospective buyers. Imagine having to remove a houseful of bright blue carpeting because the buyer lost his job between the loan approval and the closing. The earnest money deposit, usually split 50/50 between the builder and the broker in case of default, would not cover the cost of replacing the carpet.

Value Engineering

Means Illustrated Construction Dictionary defines value engineering as "A science that studies the relative value of various materials and construction techniques... considers the initial cost of construction, coupled with the estimated cost of maintenance, energy use, life expectancy, and replacement cost." The important question in value engineering is: How does the typical buyer value these materials and techniques?

Before finalizing any design, some type of value engineering process must take place. Value engineering removes cost dollars that are least valued and puts these dollars back where they are most valued. This process is far different from simply cutting costs to save money.

Value engineering involves creating more value for little or no extra cost, or lowering the cost of construction without lowering the value of the product. Reducing risk while maintaining or increasing profit is another aspect of value engineering. As much as $2.00 of savings per square foot are possible.

Size and Value

The first application of value engineering is the overall size of the home compared to the cost. For example, a large, plain box is inexpensive to build—but to appeal to the average buyer, the box needs distinguishing features, both inside and out. One such feature could be additional square footage. The construction cost of each additional square foot decreases while the appraised value of additional square footage usually remains constant. As long as the house remains within the size and price of the local market, the result will be a larger percentage of profit on the added space than on the basic package.

I always compare the area of the exterior walls to the floor areas of each plan. The cost of exterior walls (without windows or doors) should be $75 to $100 or more per lineal foot of two-story wall. A cube is the least expensive to build, but if you soften the look with a bay window or offsets in the exterior walls, you will create a more attractive product. When this type of improvement can be made without dramatically increasing the cost per square foot, it is generally worth the additional cost.

Value engineering also entails getting the most out of a floor plan. Often, portions of hallways can be converted into closet space and small areas can be opened up with half-walls and arches or by adding or relocating a window or wall. Placing furniture cutouts on a plan can illustrate wasted or tight spaces. Designing a room with possible multiple usage, such as a formal dining room with entry doors so that the room could serve as an office or temporary bedroom, is another way to value-engineer the floor plan.

The three main contributors to end value are also the items that most prospects first inquire about: bedrooms, bathrooms, and total living area. Consider the cost of adding square footage to a design to improve on these areas or to include a fourth bedroom, and compare this change to the competition. The designer must deal with the paradox between adding overall square footage to increase end value cost-effectively and holding the square footage down so the home can be offered within the target price range.

Stairways

Stairways in two-story foyers can show off a beautiful stair railing, but the cost is too high if exposed hardwood treads and fancy mill-made stair sets are also included. In my area, a popular and efficient practice allows the framing carpenter to immediately install a permanent stair using ripped 2" x 12" plank as treads with a nosing chamfer and 1" x 8" pine #2 risers. These are glued and nailed to hidden stringers that are shimmed away from the sidewall studs by 1-1/2". Sheetrock and a finish skirtboard drop nicely into this 1-1/2" gap. The railing wall is a wood-capped sloping studwall at 3" perpendicular to the tread nosing. The bottoms of the balusters are attached to the finish wood cap and a newel post extends through the cap to the floor. The overall effect is great and both labor and material are saved.

Kitchens and Baths

In the homes I've built, kitchens usually contain factory-built oak cabinets with raised-panel doors—a sought-after luxury in a move-up market. For bathroom vanities, however, I save money by dropping down a price level to the same cabinet made with flat panel doors. They look fine, are just as serviceable, and no one has ever noticed the change. Also, some of these vanity base cabinets are 18 inches deep instead of 21 inches. This means I can use an inexpensive size of molded marble top. With costs of lavatory bowls and formica vanity tops considered, I save some dollars while adding a touch of luxury to a powder room or bath.

Baths that are compartmented for use by two people at once with privacy can be used even in lower-priced homes. For a master bath, consider the vanity placed outside the bath in an alcove—then privacy is ensured during double use. Try to bring natural light into every bath. A step framed in front of a tub and covered with a proper bath floor material can create the appearance of a sunken tub, a feature generally associated with luxury baths.

The U-shaped kitchen counter work area design is always popular, but an island layout is generally considered a step up. By changing the peninsula wing of the U-shape to a small island across from the now L-shaped layout, you can add value by lowering overall costs without limiting counter space, and use less floor space while still allowing more people to work in the kitchen at the same time and adding a sought-after feature not often found in this level of home price.

In the kitchen, elimination of the wall cabinet drop ceiling saves a few dollars and provides space for display of the owner's decorative items. You may need a drop ceiling, however, for a kitchen exhaust duct or second-floor plumbing pipes. A cabinet layout that provides adequate drawer and shelf space while saving money overall is possible. Don't spend too much money providing base cabinet storage space far into blind corners—they're too difficult to reach into. Wall angle corners offer a good amount of shelf space for the money and look great. If you consult with a kitchen design specialist, you'll probably end up with a costly layout. Kitchen designers are used to dealing with remodeling homeowners who want many special features; they may also be looking for high commissions on expensive layouts. Learn to design the kitchen yourself, because hardly anyone else can relate to the spec builder's cost concerns.

A planning desk in a kitchen is desirable but not mandatory. A pantry is usually more important to buyers. I build pantries using studs, sheetrock, shelves, and a door. This provides more storage space at less cost than a factory-built pantry cabinet. This site-built pantry can contain 50 percent or more of the shelf space found in all the cabinets. With a generous pantry, you can lower the expensive cost of cabinets by using fewer of them and by avoiding the use of small, narrow cabinet boxes in the cabinet layout—they offer little space but the cost is almost the same as for a wide box.

Gourmet kitchen upgrades like angle bay dinettes; spice racks, and wine racks are great amenities, but be sure to check costs before adding them. Make sure your target market can afford these types of upgrades. One upgrade you can easily afford is tasteful and substantial-looking hardware on all cabinet doors and drawers. Often, for only $30 to $40, you can make the cabinets look extra sharp and luxurious.

Lastly, be sure to include enough kitchen counter space. Professional kitchen remodeling designers state that the struggle for adequate counter space is one of their most difficult tasks.

Closets
At a minimum, customize the master closet with a narrow stack of particleboard shelves for shoes and sweaters and use double poles at 38- and 78-inch heights. It's possible to obtain the same look advertised by custom closet remodelers for little money.

Exterior Characteristics
Some exterior details that enrich and elevate a home beyond the typical tract house are a detailed chimney top, attractive front entry, porch details, and special windows. A little extra money spent here can bring much larger returns.

Chimneys
I like to use the less expensive frame chimney shafts that house prefab metal fireplace flues. An exterior shaft costs at least $500 more than an interior chase, but this choice is seldom possible because it is often difficult to locate

the fireplace on an interior wall of the floor plan. I save siding by building the chase into the garage, and use a nicely designed wood crown or band at the top of the chimney.

Siding

Investigate all exterior wall covering options thoroughly — the appropriateness, appearance, durability, ease of locating installers, and the total costs, including nails, carpentry labor, caulking and painting, and waste.

Figure 5.3 shows my own value engineering study comparing siding costs on a particular home design. From the study I determined that this particular brand of wood composite siding cost less than aluminum, even with higher construction management costs — and I knew that wood siding had more acceptance in my target market.

Value Engineering Study

Siding Cost Comparison, Vernon Model

Aluminum siding: 24 square job @ $145 per square = $3,480.00

Wood composite siding, per cost records:

Caulk materials	$ 90
Lath for starter and corners	$ 23
Siding nails	$ 68
Siding labor (Tom)	$ 360
Siding labor (Dick)	$ 420
Siding labor (Harry)	$ 450
Siding material	$1,305
Siding flashing	$ 3
Siding paint	$ 254
Caulking labor (Harry)	$ 75
Caulking labor (Dick)	$ 25
Painting labor (Joe)	$ 75
Painting labor (Harry)	$ 250
Total	$3,398

Conclusion: This wood composite siding not only costs slightly less than an aluminum siding contract; it also has better acceptance by the market. The use of the wood composite involves more construction management time. However, the $82 cost difference is enough to compensate for this.

Figure 5.3 Value Engineering Study of Siding Costs

Windows

I have found that a job-built bay window, either angle or straight box, is less expensive than entire large units from a window manufacturer.

Skylights bring in twice the light per square foot of glass than a wall window, but problems with leaks or condensation are common with some types.
In the foyer, a light in the door, or a window adjacent to the door or over the door in the second floor wall, is less expensive than mill-made sidelites attached to the door unit.

In some areas I have seen builders use wood windows on the front elevation and less expensive vinyl windows on the remaining walls. Although this will save costs, it will be obvious to any observant prospect and will make an otherwise quality home — and its builder — look cheap.

Roofs

Roof design is an important area in which to apply value engineering. Roof trusses offer considerable overall savings over rafter construction, both in labor and materials. I use them everywhere possible except in some vaulted ceilings and where jack rafters are needed to overlay a truss roof that is at a right angle.

Higher roof pitches have become popular in recent years. They greatly improve exterior appearances with a look of shelter, strength, and proper proportion. A 5–6/12 pitch can be a real improvement. Many two-story homes today are built with 10–12/12 pitches. I don't believe such a steep slope is necessary unless you are conforming to a strict traditional design formula. Extra costs for the 1″ to 1-1/2″ increase in pitch, involving trusses, roof sheathing, roofing and larger gable areas, have amounted to less than $500 in many instances — this is a small price to pay for a greatly improved look. Figure 5.4 shows my own cost study for increasing the roof pitch on a repeated-design home. I found that for a cost of just under $400, I could build a home that appeared more substantial, more expensive, and more well-proportioned than the same home with a lower roof pitch.

Energy Issues

Because energy savings are important to the buying public, many builders are using 2″ x 6″ exterior walls instead of 2″ x 4″ walls. If these 2″ x 6″ walls are sheathed with plywood, however, they offer little more R-value than a 2″ x 4″ wall sheathed with an R-5 material. When you estimate the extra cost of the thicker wall, include increased lumber costs, carpentry labor, more stud wall insulation, wood window jamb extensions and, most important, the lost floor space calculated at a rate of at least one-half the rate for the building overall. When all the real costs are weighed against the savings in natural gas heating bills, you may find you'll realize only a 1 to 2 percent return on your investment, even in cold climates. If fuel costs quadrupled, return on the investment would be about right, but you will never be able to make up the low rate of investment returns during the first decade or two. Calculate the long-range return for the design, applying heat loss comparisons for various exterior wall types. Compare returns with a historical investment norm. You can present these calculations to buyers who question the use of a 2″ x 4″ stud wall.

Many other features have a greater effect on energy savings, such as orientation, wind tightness, house size and shape, and window manufacturer. A good wood, double-hung window with a single pane of glass and separate storm window offers more resistance to air infiltration and the same R-value as a 1/2″ thermopane without a storm window.

Exterior Sidewall Stud Spacing

In some markets, exterior stud walls at 24 inches on center are used. This saves some money but presents some problems, too. Certain exterior sidings look wavy over them and, on the interior, there may not be a stud for attaching a wall cabinet.

Value Engineering Study of Roof Pitch Increase from 4^6 to 6^0	
Cost of 6/12 roof on Highlander model, with 9/12 front gable, 15/35 casing in master bedroom:	
Rafter length of 30′ home:	6/12 = 19′-0″ 4^6/12 = 18′-2″
Trusses:	Extra cost each @ +/− $2.00 × 31 ea. = 62 + 5% = $65
Rough carpentry:	No extra charge
Gable end, increase in area:	+/− 100 sq. ft. @ $1.35 + .25 (siding/sheath) = $160
Extra soffit and fascia:	12′ @ .90 plus tax = $12
Extra roof sheathing:	8 sheets × 32 sq. ft. = 256 sq. ft. @ .21 = $56 plus tax = $59
Extra roofing:	2 extra courses; 1-1/3 squares @ $45 = $60 2′ taller fireplace chase: 2′ × 12 (2 × 4) = 24 or 16 B.M. @ 300 = $5; 12′ × 2′ = 24 sq. ft. (O.S.B.) @ .20 = $5; siding 16 sq. ft. @ 1.35 = $22; corners 4 × 2′ = 8′ @ .50 = $4. $5 + $5 + $22 + $4 = $36
2′ of fireplace pipe:	$20
Window change:	32/20 D.H. = $192.75 15/35 casing = − 161.55 31.20 (−37%) = $19.66 plus tax = ($21)
Total cost:	$391.00

Figure 5.4 Value Engineering Study of Roof Pitch Increase from 4^6 to 6^0

Value Engineering and Perceived Value

Use the principles of value engineering in every planning decision. Provide only what the consumer will pay for and truly needs. Evaluate every decision's net effect on value, marketability, and cost. Never sacrifice marketability for cost saving. These value judgments must be both qualitative and quantitative.

Value engineering often deals with fads, fashions, or beauty — *perceived* value. Learn to modify existing designs to make them more attractive than the competition. All this takes time and sometimes more detailed drawings, but time thus spent returns the most dollars per house.

Preliminary Sketches

Although you may not execute the final working drawings, it is advantageous to do preliminary sketches in an effort to closely control the design process. Only you have the coordinated knowledge of the local market, the site, and neighboring homes.

A sketch may begin with a simple collection of intersecting circles or bulbs to represent rooms, or maybe some redrawn lines over a plan from a newspaper or competitor's brochure. As soon as possible, you should move to a drafting board, where everything can be laid out to scale (1/4″ or more), including actual room sizes. If you don't begin a scale preliminary drawing early in the design process, you may put too much effort into work that will not fit into the overall house area limits. Exterior elevation problems can also be detected early with a scale sketch. Again, scale furniture cutouts can be helpful to check room sizes and shapes. A great deal of creativity is needed at this stage. It won't flow out of you over one continuous work period. Be patient. You may need many rest periods before your creativity is fully utilized.

It is best to design several elevations and both floors of a two-story home concurrently. You can use a good house design reference book, your own experience, and the building code book to design dimensions for stairs, kitchen layouts, and closets. Catalogs illustrating windows, cabinets, metal fireplaces, and unusual fixtures are also necessary tools. If you hire a design consultant to do this work, stay very closely involved. Remember your design objective: the best, most appealing house for the money when compared to the competition.

Comprehensive Working Drawings

In general, most working drawings used by small builders are poorly drawn and incomplete. When drawing final plans, be sure to do a professional job. Subcontractors tend to have more respect for a builder who furnishes a plan that is complete and easy to read. This respect translates into quicker and closer bid prices and better performance on the job.

Drawing the final plans can be time-consuming, so I suggest hiring a good draftsperson or designer who is thorough and neat. The hourly or package cost for this service can be less than for a good finish trim carpenter. No matter who executes the final drawing, expect to make some changes and corrections after seeing the finished plans.

Final plans as well as preliminaries are usually drawn on 18″ × 24″ technical paper. The rough carpentry subcontractor will spend the most time referring to the plans, so be sure they are drawn with his needs as first priority. The plans must indicate dimensions, wall thicknesses, and room sizes from outside of exterior wall sheathing to interior stud face and across the room to the opposite stud face. With this system of dimensioning, the lead carpenter's mental arithmetic at the job site can be held to a minimum, resulting in fewer errors.

It is important to make these kinds of small details clear so the job is as straightforward as possible. This will minimize the number of mistakes made and thereby save money. Here are some other guidelines for simplicity and clarity:

- Make sure foundation column footings are of adequate size to support the concentrated column loads.
- Locate forced-air furnaces as close as possible to the center of the plan.
- Keep as many dimension lines and numbers as possible *outside* the floor plan for ease of reading.
- Locate circuit breakers so as to minimize the length of expensive 200-volt wire.
- Use a consistent system of dimensioning and detailing.
- Don't crowd too much detail into any one area of the sheet—ease of reading is critical. Plans will generally be used at a noisy, windy job site, not on a clean desk in a quiet office.
- List accurately the square footage of each floor and of the garage on the plans.
- Lay all floor joists and roof trusses in the same direction when using forced air heating.
- Furnish the rough size of the basement stairwell, as well as the location, on the carpenter's plan.
- Be conservative in the number of electrical outlets and switches. You will need an idea of the kitchen or bath light fixtures that might be used when drawing these outlets on the plan.

Any details that are not necessary for bidding or that apply to only one trade can be drawn on a final sheet that is furnished later, when needed for construction. Plans that appear too overloaded with extra pages of special details have a way of eliciting high bids from subs. For example, an electrical plan attached to the electrician's plan set or, for the carpenter, an extra sheet showing rough window openings, header sizes, floor or roof framing plans, porch details, and stair details, can be attached to a set of plans later.

During the late days of construction, some buyer prospects, and most likely the ultimate buyer, will want to examine the plans. Neat, well-done plans can be an important selling tool. You might give the front elevation a bit of a pictorial touch by using a heavy dark line on the roof ridges, eaves, and base grade line. Add a few foundation plantings or background trees. These extra touches will help the prospective buyer to picture the final product.

Specifications

If you finance your spec home with a construction loan, the lender will ask for a set of specifications along with your plans, for use by an appraiser. Even if you don't use a construction loan, I recommend that you complete, or at least partially finish, the specification documents within the first month of construction. I use the four-page HUD form, "Description of Materials," after making a few changes to fit my location and type of construction. Figure 5.5 is a reproduction of this form, completed for a home that I built several years ago.

Fully complete whatever form you use during construction as soon as interior choices are finalized. This is important so that if a serious buyer is willing to commit at an early stage, the document will detail what is included in the purchase price and be ready for signatures.

In the event of a contradiction between plans and specifications, the specifications have priority, unless there is a full-size detail on the plan set. The specifications also serve as a reference when obtaining bids and purchasing. The buyer's mortgage lender and appraiser will need a copy.

Dollar allowances, included in the total home price for items selected by the buyers after their loan approval, can be set forth in the specifications. For example, under floor covering, set up a dollar allowance to cover the cost of carpeting, pad, installation, and sales tax. List a close approximation of the total carpet yardage. Specify that buyers agree to pay any upgrading charges, over allowance, prior to installation. Light fixtures can be handled in the same way. Allowances are discussed further in Chapter 9.

List exact names, models, and numbers of mechanical equipment, appliances, and plumbing fixtures. Be specific about roofing, special shelves in closets, paints and number of coats, special millwork items, and finish hardware. Describe species of wood, mirror sizes and thicknesses, gauges of sheet metal, and telephone outlets. Call out items that are not included in the price such as landscaping, seed bed preparation, exterior pavements, drapery rods, and survey work for the buyer's mortgagee. Normally I include all cleanup work and trash hauling, but glass cleaning is limited to a "once over" job. Final glass cleaning is done by buyers.

Here are some of the ideas I use in my specifications:

- Energy-saving features whose cost could not be paid back in six to seven years are not used unless they are inexpensive to purchase.
- Roof-mounted attic exhaust fans are an excellent cost-saving feature and generally cost only $50 to $75.
- Good kitchen lighting is a must, but be wary of too much artificial light.
- Formica kitchen counters (instead of tile) can make a small area appear larger.
- Central vacuum-cleaning systems are very costly and usually lack the important carpet-beating action of portable vacuums.
- Special interior woodwork items such as crown moldings, chair rails, and ceiling beams are generally not specified. If the buyer wants and is willing to pay for these items, they can be installed before the sale closing.

Description of Materials

NO.

BUILDING CONTRACT- NOT A SPEC   DATE 2/3/89

PROPERTY ADDRESS   LOT 19   CITY   STATE

MORTGAGOR/OWNER   WILLIAM AND MARY SMITH

CONTRACTOR OR BUILDER   JOHN DOE- BUILDER

1. Excavation:

Bearing soil, type   FIRM CLAY

2. Foundations:

Footings: Concrete mix   5 BAG   Reinforcing

Foundation wall: Material   5 BAG CONCRETE (8")   Reinforcing (2) 1/2" REBAR

Interior foundation wall: Material   N.A.   Party foundation wall

Columns: Material and size   3 1/2" Ø STEEL   Piers: Material and reinforcing

Girders: Material and sizes   I BEAM STEEL - 8" @ 18 #   Sills: Material

Basement entrance areaway   NONE   Window areaways   GALV. STEEL (2)- 12"

Waterproofing   TAR COATING   Footing drains   POLYETHYLENE DRAIN TUBING (4")

                                                    WITH STONE COVERING, TO INSIDE SUMP.

Basementless space: Ground cover   N.A.   Insulation 1" STYROFOAM FROM GRADE LEVEL TO 4' BELOW.

Special foundations   4' DEEP FTG. & 6" CONC. WALL UNDER GARAGE. (2) HAUNCH WALLS (CONC.) FOR FRONT STOOP.

3. Chimneys:

Material GALV. METAL - FIRE PLACE & WATER HEATER   Prefabricated (make and size) 3" I.D. CLASS B &
                                                                                    (2) WALL FIREPLACE FLUE

Flue lining: Material   Heater flue size   Fireplace flue size

Vents (material and size): Gas or oil heater   PLASTIC PIPE FOR FURNACE EXHAUST.   Water heater 3" I.D. CLASS B
                                               GALV. CHIMNEY CHASE TOP.

4. Fireplaces:

Construction FACTORY BUILT; SEARS "38B SUPERIOR" (GLASS DOORS NOT INCLUDED)

Firebox REFRACTORY CERAMIC & STEEL/OUTSIDE COMB. AIR Flue 8"- 12 1/2" (2) WALL STEEL

Interior facing BRICK: "MIDLAND," COLONIAL RED   Hearth MIDLAND COLONIAL RED 1/2 PAVERS

Mantle OAK TOP, APRON, ARCH BOARDS & SIDE FRAMES — PER PLANS

5. Exterior Walls:

Studs 2" x 4" @ 16" O.C.   Headers 2" x 8" & 12"   Plates 2" x 4"

Wood frame: Grade and species STANDARD & BETTER HEM-FIR   Sill sealer FIBERGLASS

Sheathing STYROFOAM   thickness 1"   Corner bracing: 1" x 4" FIR

Siding RUF CEDAR grade KNOTTY   type BEVELED   size 3/4" x 8"   exposure 6 1/8"   fastening GALV. NAILS

5/4" x 5"- 6" RUF CEDAR CORNER BOARDS. 1" RUF CEDAR ON BAY WINDOWS.

Masonry veneer N.A.   Sills   Lintels

Door sills CONCRETE   Window sills PINE   Lintels NONE

Figure 5.5 Description of Materials Form

5. Exterior Walls (continued):

furring

Exterior painting: Material & LABOR & CAULKING BY BUYERS   number of coats

"MAXAM 2" & "MAXAM 4" SUGGESTED FOR SIDING & TRIM. ALKYD PRIMER FOR TRIM.

6. Floor Framing: 2" x 10" @ 16" O.C.

Joists: Wood, grade and species STANDARD & BETTER DOUG. FIR   bridging 1" x 3"   anchors

Concrete slab: [X] basement floor [ ] first floor [ ] ground supported [ ] self-supporting   mix 5 BAG   thickness 3"

reinforcing   insulation   membrane

Fill under slab: Material CRUSHED LIMESTONE   thickness 4" - 6"

7. Subflooring: (Describe underflooring for special boards under item 21.)

Material: Grade and species ORIENTED STRAND BOARD 4' x 8'   size 3/4"   type T & G

Laid: [X] first floor [X] second floor GLUE & NAIL

8. Finish Flooring & Floor Covering: ARMSTRONG "SUNDIAL SOLARIUM" SHEET VINYL FOR LAUN., KIT., DINETTE, LWR. BATH,

MAIN UPPER BATH. FOYER /GUEST CLOSET: 8"X 8" CERAMIC TILE "CINNAMON PROMENADE" IN FLEXI-GROUT. VINYL &

TILE AREAS LAID OVER 1/4" LUAN PLYWD. UNDERLAYMT. BAL. OF FLOORS & UPPER STAIRS TO BE CARPETED.
CONTRACT INCL. AN ALLOWANCE OF $2000 TO COVER CARPTING, PAD, LABOR & TAX (APPROX. 180 YDS.). ALL
MATLS. MUST BE IMMED. AVAIL. IN METRO AREA. BUYERS PAY ANY ALLOW. OVERAGE PRIOR TO INSTALLATION.

9. Partition Framing:

Studs: Wood, grade and species STD & BTR. HEM-FIR Size and spacing 2" x 4" @ 16" O.C.

Plates STD & BTR. HEM-FIR   Headers 4"x 4" HEM-FIR OR PER PLAN

10. Ceiling Framing:

Joists: Wood, grade, and species STD & BTR. DOUG. FIR 2"x 10" @ 16" O.C.   Bridging 1" x 3"

11. Roof Framing: ENGINEERED ROOF TRUSSES @ 24" O.C.

Rafters: Wood, grade and species   Roof trusses (see detail): Grades and species

12. Roofing:

Sheathing: Grade and species ORIENTED STRAND BOARD   size 4' x 8'   type 1/2" W/ PLYCLIPS @ MID SPAN

Roofing 3 TAB ASHPHALT SHINGLES, SELF- SEALING   weight or thickness 240# size 12"X 36" fastening NAILS

Underlay

Built-up roofing   number of plies   surfacing material

Flashing: Material GALV. METAL   gauge or weight 26 GA. [ ] gravel stops

13. Gutters and Downspouts:

Gutters: Material FACT. ENAMEL STEEL, WHITE gauge or weight 26 GA.   size 4"   shape BOX

Downspouts: Material "   "   " gauge or weight 26 GA.   size   shape BOX   number

14. Drywall:

[X] walls [X] ceilings   Material GYPSUM   thickness 1/2" (5/8" ON TRUSSES) joint treatment TAPE

5/8" ON GARAGE FIREWALL   texture or finish SAND

15. Decorating: (Paint, wallpaper, stain, varnish, enamel)

Rooms	Wall Finish Material and Application	Ceiling Finish Material and Application

ALL DRYWALL SURFACES PAINTED (SPRAYED) WITH OFF-WHITE "HERCOFLAT" WASHABLE LATEX

Figure 5.5 Description of Materials Form (cont'd)

16. Decorating (continued):

PAINT FROM HALLMAN PAINT CO. BY BUILDER. FINAL TOUCH-UP BY BUYERS. WOODWORK: (1) COAT "MINWAX" #211 STAIN, (2) COATS "JAMES DAY" POLYURETHANE SEALER & VARNISH EXCEPT NO STAIN ON CLOSET SHELVES, BACK OF SLIDING DOORS, BASEMENT STAIRS, CLOSET HOOKSTRIPS & POLES. LABOR & MATERIAL FOR ALL WOODWORK DECORATING BY BUYER.

16. Interior Doors and Trim:

Doors: Type FLUSH, HOLLOW CORE   material OAK   thickness 1 3/8"

Door trim: Type COLONIAL   material OAK- 2 1/4"   Base: Type RANCH-2 5/8"   material OAK   size

Finish: Doors SAME AS WOODWORK   trim SAME AS DOORS

Slide-by doors: SAME AS ABOVE

Jambs OAK   trim COLONIAL CASING   finish

17. Windows   NOTE: "OAKUM" STUFFED UNDER ALL SILLS FOR WIND DRAFT.

Make and model: "HURD" REMOVABLE.

Windows DOUBLE-HUNG (SLIDE-BY IN BASEMENT)   material PINE

Glass: Grade & type SSB - SINGLE GLAZE, EXCEPT THERMO. FOR FOYER   head flashing GALV. METAL

Trim: Type COLONIAL   material OAK- 2 1/4"   finish WOODWORK   number of coats 3

Weatherstripping: Type FACTORY VINYL   hardware FACTORY

Storms/screens "HURD" COMBINATION   number ALL, EXCEPT GARAGE   screen cloth material VINYL

Basement windows: Type SLIDING   material METAL   ☒ screens, number 2   ☒ Storm sash, number 2

Special windows FOYER: FIXED THERMO GLAZED CASEMENT. (2) OCTAGON WINDOWS w/ STORMS. REMOVABLE DIVIDED LITE GRILLES FOR UPPER 1/2 OF FRONT WINDOWS & OCTAGONS ONLY.

18. Entrances and Exterior Detail:

Main entrance door: Material FIR "NICOLAI" #2020   thickness 1 3/4"   Frame: Material PINE   thickness 1"

Other entrance doors: Material STEEL FIRE DOOR   thickness 1 3/4"   Frame: Material PINE   thickness 1"

Head flashing N.A.   Weatherstripping: Type COMPRESSION   saddles OAK & ALUM.

(1) LITE, (3) PANEL, FIR "PHOENIX" GARAGE SERVICE DOOR

Combination storm and screen doors: (1) "PHOENIX" WOOD CROSS BUCK

Paint LATEX EXT. TRIM   number of coats 2

Entry door design FAN LITE BY "NICOLAI"

19. Cabinets, Vanities, Counters:

Kitchen cabinets, make and model MERRILAT'S MEADOW OAK (SAME DESIGN UPPER & LOWER). HANDLES, IF ANY, BY BUYERS.   Counter top FORMICA   edging SINGLE COVE

Back and end splash SINGLE COVE   Finish of cabinets FACTORY   number of coats

Medicine cabinets: Make NONE   model

Other cabinets MERRILAT'S HOMESTEAD OAK (BACK OF KITCHEN PENINSULA CABINETS TO BE OLDE ENGLISH OAK BY ROSEBURG.)

Vanities MERRILAT'S HOMESTEAD OAK. FORMICA TOPS FOR DESK & UPPER VANITIES.

Figure 5.5 Description of Materials Form (cont'd)

20. Stairs:

Stair	Treads		Risers		Stringers		Handrail		Balusters	
	Material	Thickness	Material	Thickness	Material	Size	Material	Size	Material	Size
Basement	PINE	1 1/8"	PINE	3/4"	FIR	2" x 12"	PINE	ROUND	NONE	
Main	FIR	1 1/2"	PINE	3/4"	FIR	2" x 10"	HEMLOCK #6010			
Attic										

HEMLOCK "ACORN" NEWEL POST & SLENDER BALUSTERS FOR APPROX. 3' OF LOWER STAIR @ (2) BALUSTERS PER TREAD ON OAK CAPPED SKIRT WALL. MAIN STAIRS TO HAVE OAK SKIRTS.

21. Special:

CAPPED 1/2 WALLS TO BE 3/4" OAK WITH ROUTED DETAIL EDGES & BASE STOPS UNDER. LOWER BATH VANITY TO HAVE MOLDED MARBLE TOP. STALL SHOWER DOOR "WISC. SHR. DR." SLIDING GLASS IN SILVER SATIN METAL FRAME. SHOWER CURTAIN ROD FOR TUB. CERAMIC TILE AT WHIRLPOOL TUB ("NATIONAL" #304, 6'x3') TO BE 6"x6" MONARCH BLUE CLOUD, GLOSSY SHADOW SERIES, COLOR #478, ABOVE (3) SIDES OF TUB & OVER ADJ. LEDGE, TO ± 18" ABOVE TUB.

Bathroom accessories SURFACE MOUNTED ANTIQUE BRASS FIXTURES BY "MIAMI CAREY". (3) TOILET PAPER HOLDERS AND (5) TOWEL BARS.

22. Plumbing:

Fixture	Number	Location	Make	Model	Size	Color
Sink	1	KITCHEN	KOHLER - "BROOKFIELD" CAST IRON		30" x 22"	ALMOND
Lavatory	3	UPPER BATHS	MANSFIELD CHINA, SELF- RIMMING		OVAL	ALMOND
Water closet	3	BATHS	MANSFIELD, WATER SAVER			ALMOND
Bathtub	1	MAIN BATH	FIBERGLASS MODULE		5'	BONE
Shower over tub	YES					
Stall shower	1	MASTER BATH	FIBERGLASS MODULE		4'	BONE
Laundry tray		DOUBLE TRAY TUB — IN BASEMENT				
Washer connection		YES - AT TUB				
Floor drain	1	BASEMENT & SUMP W/ PUMP: REAR YARD DISCHARGE PER CODE.				
Faucets	ALL	SINGLE LEVER: "DELTA" IN KITCHEN, MOEN "CHATEAU" IN REMAINDER.				

☒ Curtain rod   ☒ Door   ☐ Curtain rod

Water supply: ☒ public   ☐ community system   ☐ individual (private) system

Sewage disposal: ☒ public   ☐ community system   ☐ individual (private) system

House drain (inside): ☐ cast iron   ☐ tile   ☒ other   PVC PLASTIC

Water piping: ☐ galvanized steel   ☒ copper tubing   ☐ other   Sill cocks, number 2

Domestic water heater: Type GAS   make and model

recovery   gph. 100' rise.   Storage tank: Material   capacity 50 gallons

Gas service: ☒ utility company   ☐ liq. pet. gas   ☐ other   Gas piping: ☐ cooking   ☒ house heating   ☒ dryer

WATER LINES FOR FUTURE SOFTENER, BUT NO SOFTENER INCLUDED.

Figure 5.5 Description of Materials Form (cont'd)

23. Heating & Ventilating:

"TEMPSTAR" (HEIL - WHIRLPOOL) HI-EFFICIENCY, FORCED AIR GAS FURNACE, 75,000 Btu
WITH CONTROLS AND VENTING AS REQUIRED BY CODE. WARM AIR OUTLETS IN
BASEMENT, FIRST & SECOND FLOORS. RETURN AIR OUTLETS IN BASEMENT,
FIRST & SECOND FLOORS (OK FOR ANY A/C UNIT). ROUND HONEYWELL THERMOSTAT
IN FORMAL DINING ROOM. INCLUDES RETURN AIRS FOR BEDROOMS.
NO CENTRAL A/C UNIT OR WIRING FOR SAME. NO CLOTHES CHUTE.
POWER ATTIC FAN: "LESLIE/LOCKE" MODEL MD 105.

Roof vents   PER CODE   eave vents   PER CODE

Bath fan vents   (3) BROAN

Range fan vents   (1) TO OUTSIDE & (1) DRYER VENT THRU JOIST SKIRT

24. Electric Wiring: INC. (4) TELEPHONE OUTLETS UPSTAIRS & (1) AT KITCHEN COUNTER

Service: ☐ overhead ☒ underground   Panel: ☐ fuse box ☒ circuit breaker 200 AMP   Outlets: number APPROX. 117

Wiring: ☐ conduit ☐ armored cable ☒ nonmetallic cable ☐ knob and tube ☒ other WHIRLPOOL

Special outlets: ☒ range ☐ water heater ☒ other WHIRLPOOL, FURNACE, DISHWASHER, SUMP

☒ Doorbell ☒ Chimes   Push-button locations FRONT & REAR PATIO DOOR

Vent fans   (3) BATH FANS   Smoke detectors 1 PER FLOOR, PER CODE

25. Lighting Fixtures

Total number of fixtures APPROX. 17   Total allowance for fixtures, typical installation, $ 500.

NET COST, INC. SALES TAX, IS ALLOWANCE INC. IN PRICE OF HOME.
OUTDOOR DRIVE LITE REQUIRED BY COVENANTS W/IN ONE YEAR IS NOT INC., BUT IN-
HOUSE WIRING IS READY FOR IT, WITH SWITCH.

26. Insulation:

Location	Thickness	Material, Type, and Method of Installation	"R" Factor	Vapor Barrier
Roof	15"	BLOWN FIBERGLASS WOOL	38	4 MIL POLYETHYL.
Ceiling				
Wall	3½"	FRICTION FIT FIBERGLASS BATTS	13	4 MIL POLYETHYL.
Floor	6" (OVERHANG) FRICTION FIT FIBERGLASS BATTS		19	
Box Sill	6"	FRICTION FIT FIBERGLASS BATTS	19	

27. Miscellaneous: (Describe any main dwelling materials, equipment, or construction items not shown elsewhere.)

Sliding glass doors (1) "PARKVIEW"   size 6' - WOOD   make & model 1" INSUL. GLASS

lock LATCH   INCLUDES SLIDING SCREEN

Interior of closets & pantry PARTICLE BOARD SHELVES: 5-16" IN LINEN, 6-16" IN PANTRY. POLE &
12" SHELVES IN CLOTHES CLOSETS. MASTER CLOSET HAS DBL. POLE ON SHORT WALL &
5-12" SHOE SHELVES. FINISH FOR THESE ITEMS — (1) COAT SEALER.

Finish hardware: entry locksets "COPA" BY KWIKSET — (3) KEYED ALIKE, U.S. 5 FINISH.

Other locksets SAME, W/ PRIVACY FOR M. BED. & BATHS; BALANCE ARE PASSAGE.

Mirrors (3) ¼" PLATE, SQUARE EDGE: 24"x 36" FOR LOWER BATH, (2) 48"x 36" FOR UPPERS.

Figure 5.5 Description of Materials Form (cont'd)

27. Miscellaneous (continued):

Bath towel bars & paper holders   SEE ITEM 21.

Door closer   NONE REQUIRED.

28. Special Equipment (Appliances): (State material or make and model.)

Automatic washer   BY BUYERS   Kitchen range   BUYER'S EXISTING ELEC. RANGE

Clothes dryer   BY BUYERS   Refrigerator   BY BUYERS

Dishwasher   SEARS 24" MODEL 14165   Other   RANGE HOOD

Garbage disposal unit   BADGER I, BY INSINKERATER

29. Porches & Decks:

Conc. porches   10'x 4', FRONT ENTRY   door sills   CONCRETE (1)

Wood deck or patio door step   BY BUYERS

30. Clean-up & Trash Hauling: BY BUYERS

SPIC & SPAN FINE GLASS CLEANING BY BUYERS

31. Garages and Overhead Doors:

16'x 7' & 8' x 7' FLUSH, 1³/₈" THICK. ELECTRIC DOOR OPERATORS NOT INCLUDED.

Overhead door: make and model   "LIFETIME"   style   SMOOTH FLUSH

springs   TORSION FOR BOTH   glazing   NONE

jambs and outside trim   1" x 6" PINE & BRICK MOLDING

32. Driveways: AS PART OF $450 LAND IMPROVEMENT ALLOWANCE.

Driveway: Width 12' & MORE   Base material #2 STONE   thickness 4"   Surfacing material NONE   thickness

Front walk: Width NONE material   thickness   Service walk: Width   material   thickness

Steps: Material NONE   treads   risers

ADDITIONAL 3" OF CRUSHED LIMESTONE TO BE INC. GUEST PARKING TO BE INC. AT TIME

OF FINAL GRADING (AFTER SHEETROCK DEL.) AS PART OF $450 LAND IMPROVEMENT ALLOW.

33. Other On-Site Improvements: (Specify all exterior on-site improvements not described elsewhere, including items such as unusual grading, drainage structures, retaining walls, fence, railings, and accessory structures.)

Finish grading   OF LOT AS NEEDED, INC. SPREADING OF ON-SITE TOPSOIL, AFTER COMPLETION

OF UNDERGROUND UTILITIES & CONCRETE / SHEETROCK DELIVERY.

Water service   BY LATERALS TO STREET MAINS

Sewer service   BY LATERAL TO STREET MAINS, AS PER LAND IMPROVEMENT ALLOWANCE.

NOT INCLUDED BY BUILDER: LANDSCAPING / SEED BED PREPARATION, EXTERIOR PAVEMENT,

WATER SOFTENER / FILTER, DRAPERY / CURTAIN RODS, WALLPAPER, MORTGAGEE LOT

SURVEY, CROWN MOLDINGS, CHAIR RAILS.

Identification—This exhibit shall be identified by the signature of the builder, or sponsor, and/or the proposed mortgagor if the latter is known at the time of the application.

Date   Signature

Builder   Signature

Figure 5.5 Description of Materials Form (cont'd)

Changes: Before, During, and After Construction

No matter how much time you spend developing a new home model, improvements will need to be made. Scrutinize the design and specifications constantly: it is the only way to make improvements. Make all possible improvements to the plan as soon as possible. Write down any design ideas or actual changes in the job notebook, which you should carry with you every day. You may realize the need for an improvement too late for the home under construction, but make a note to incorporate the change into the next home. Brokers, buyers, neighbors, and even building tradespeople may offer suggestions.

After the home is occupied, visit the buyers. Listen carefully to their comments and note how their furnishings and lifestyle fit the design. This information will be helpful to you when designing and/or building future homes.

To help sell a product during tough markets, one change I have made after construction is to build a wood deck. A prospective buyer will generally pay more attention to the yard and the natural landscape if there is a deck to step out onto instead of mud. At other times, I've changed partition locations, added a coat closet off the garage entry, or changed door swings and door designs at the last moment in the construction process.

Architectural Board Approvals

Many local, municipal, and/or subdivision architectural boards will require approval of plans and some specifications prior to beginning construction. If these approvals are not required from anyone except the zoning board, this may be an indication that the location is not in a very desirable subdivision or community.

Some architectural requirements are written into the subdivision covenants. They may state, for example: "Two-story homes must have 1,200 square feet on the first floor and 2,000 square feet total"; "All exteriors will be covered with natural materials"; "Some brick or masonry veneers will be used on all sides of the home"; "Homes must be of a traditional Williamsburg Colonial design"; "Fireplaces are encouraged, but if not included, two flues shall project from the chimney top to create the appearance of a fireplace."

The Negative Aspects

Sometimes architectural approval consists only of a quick glance by one or two people. Unfortunately, I have on occasion worked with boards of six or more appointed individuals who are not qualified by either training or experience—they are not able to properly read a set of plans, are inconsistent in their approach, and are politically motivated. I have witnessed jealousy and competitive reactions from subdivision architectural board members as well. For example, I once presented plans that used exterior wall coverings that had been used on other homes recently built in the subdivision. However, on my home I was asked to use costly upgrades in these coverings by members of the board for no apparent reason. I later learned that one person was having difficulty in selling his 15-year-old home near the subdivision, and hoped a luxury look on my exterior would help his sale.

In some communities, architectural boards are required to approve exterior colors. Window style, treatment, and placement are also closely reviewed. For example, the board might request that shutters be used for every window whether or not it suits the style of the home.

Case Study:
Subdividers May Make Unacceptable Demands

A subdivider who had granted me approval in a slightly better-grade subdivison turned down my more luxurious design in a new subdivision. He wanted me to add wide exterior wood surrounds to all windows. I backed out because I was already slightly over budget for the neighborhood and apprehensive about what the other homes and duplexes surrounding my product would look like. The general location in the community was marginal, at best. Perhaps he was trying to use my house to upgrade his poor location.

The Positive Aspect

Despite these experiences, architectural boards can have a positive effect. Many of their comments and requirements are helpful. If you are a new builder in a community with a board, attend one or two of their meetings before submitting plans. Meet face to face with subdividers who can give insight into subdivision architectural approval.

Case Study:
Neighbors May Make Uninformed Demands

I encountered a problem when building on one of the few remaining unbuilt lots in a subdivision. I had no problem obtaining municipal architectural approval and there was no longer a subdivision committee in this older subdivision. However, two weeks later I was informed of a petition of objection brought by the surrounding neighbors. Because of this, a building permit could not be issued. State law gave the neighbors 48 hours after board approval to object to any plan, provided they obtain a certain number of signatures.

Two sisters who owned several vacant lots nearby had circulated the petition. They claimed to have inspected the plans at the city building department and felt that too little brickwork was to be used at the front entry. The sisters doubted that the home would be worth as much as $125,000. The first petition signature they obtained was from a nearby nephew. The nephew took it across the street to a family that vacationed with them, for their signature. And so it went. Only the sisters bothered to visit city hall to inspect the plans. The others accepted the plan as described by the sisters.

I finally convinced the sisters to meet with me at the building inspector's office. After viewing the plans in my presence, they realized that the brickwork was more extensively specified. They agreed to obtain new signatures and release the objection. We built the home as originally planned and sold it for over $130,000.

Economies of Repetition and the Builder's Own Residence

"When contentment comes through the door, improvement goes out the window." — Anonymous

Thorough plans, specifications, material lists, and color selections are necessary to efficiently build any home. Because these items require a fair amount of work, building the same design more than once will save a lot of paperwork and estimating and purchasing time, and increase control over quality and profits.

Once you have developed a profitable plan that is well received by the market, why not lower the risk by staying with it? With each duplication, new ways to save time, improve design, and save on materials and labor will emerge. Try to utilize this strategy as much as possible; otherwise you will continually have to "reinvent the wheel." Although plan repetition requires selecting sites that suit a particular plan, this is usually more profitable than having to develop a new plan to fit a rugged or narrow bargain site.

It is important, however, for any builder to remain aware of market changes and keep design skills current. Be sure to modify repeated designs when necessary and occasionally add a new plan to your line of products.

An excellent way for you to challenge a design that will be used repetitively is to live in the completed home. Many builders work for a long time before they live in one of their own homes. This is the real test of a product. Another great advantage is in having a furnished, completed model of a home under construction. Buyers are notoriously bad at visualizing what the finished home will look like. Being able to show a prospect a finished, furnished home is a powerful sales tool.

Summary

There are probably hundreds, maybe even thousands, of considerations to pursue in the design of a new home. Market research and a study of good home plans are valuable in creating a successful spec home design. In addition to the layout of the rooms in the house, it is equally important to consider the effects of natural light, the landscape, interior and exterior colors, and the lines and angles of the house. And again, the best way to test your home design is to live in it yourself.

Key Points
- Other builders are a great source of design ideas. Other sources of ideas are large building firms' use of detailed drawings, stock plans by mail, and certain builder magazines.
- The cost of preliminary sketches and design work is about one-third the total design cost.
- If you are building spec homes, you should have an understanding of various engineering concepts, such as loads, spans, and related calculations.
- A spec home should incorporate features that have local acceptance but have not been widely offered by the competition.
- Provide perceived space and elegance with a minimum of overall floor space and exterior wall surface.

- Avoid plans that are difficult to build; that require long, skillful hours to frame; and that use framing materials in excess.
- In designing and building spec homes, plan for the effects of sunlight.
- Curb appeal is enhanced by a strong front elevation; effective use of siding; attractive roof pitches; the use of at least one gable; a well-proportioned porch; and window alignment and appearance.
- Be sure to use exterior colors that fit the style of the home.
- Use the interior color scheme to enlarge the space with continuous, light colors. Stay with traditional, time-tested colors in paint, tile, and floor coverings.
- Use value engineering to compare the overall size of the home to its cost — get the most out of your floor plan. The three main contributors to end value are bedrooms, bathrooms, and total living area.
- Plans that are overloaded with extra pages of special details tend to elicit high bids from subs.
- Building the same plan more than once will save a lot of paperwork and estimating and purchasing time.
- Remain aware of market changes and keep design skills current.
- The best way to evaluate a design is to live in the completed home yourself.

Chapter 6
Lists, Bids, & Purchasing: Materials & Subcontractor Selections

When I was building one of my first spec homes, I had three bids for carpentry from union subcontractors with good references. The bids ranged from $2,700 to $3,000. I also received a fourth bid of $3,500 from a non-union contractor. I decided to hire the carpenter whose bid was $2,700 but before I did, a friend told me of a contractor he had met in a local tavern. Despite some reservations, I contacted him. As it turned out, he was a well-established carpentry contractor with 10 to 20 employees. His bid was $2,250 and his work and service were excellent.

Builders often shop around considerably to save money on small items (that cost under $200), yet solicit only one or two bids on a subcontract that runs over $5,000. The bulk of purchasing effort should be spent on the largest categories of cost. It is wise to obtain three bids for the lowest-cost items and four to six bids for larger items. It pays to shop around.

Before you continue to read this chapter, you should have an understanding of the terminology that will be used. *Purchasing* involves selecting a firm, a price, a method, or a material. *Expediting* gets these materials and services to the job at an appointed time. Finally, *supervision* is the direction and inspection of the actual on-site work.

Strategies for Higher Quality and Lower Prices

Everyone knows the old saying, "You only get what you pay for." Although this is generally true of building materials, it does not apply to subcontractors. In general, I have not found a consistent relationship between price and quality on subcontracted work. The lowest bidder often delivers good quality work. Therefore, quality of work cannot be judged simply on bid price. Labor efficiencies, advanced equipment, low wages, a zero net profit expectation, and low overhead can all affect a subcontractor's bid price.

Be thorough when searching for subcontractors to bid work. Finding good subcontractors is rewarding work; but if you are working in a new area, this may be one of your most difficult tasks. Sources for finding subcontractors include the following:

• Various suppliers, such as ready-mix or concrete block manufacturers

- Lumber yards and millwork and window dealers
- The local builder's association and visits to their "Parade of Homes"
- Newspaper advertisements, including all the small community free "advertisers"
- The yellow pages in phone books for very wide geographical areas

The best way to find subcontractors is to drive around neighborhoods where new homes are being built. There you will find a number of subcontractors and suppliers at work. This method also provides a chance to evaluate the quality of work being performed and observe the tradespeople themselves prior to soliciting a bid from subs that are utilized by other professional builders. Remember, many good subs have no office away from home, no business phone, and no name on their vehicles.

If you are a new builder, or new to an area, you should get about eight bids in each category. I once sought twelve bids on rough carpentry. I had returned to my home state after a six-year absence and a boom was underway. Subs were busy and independent. Many bids were in the $7,000 to $8,000 range. A few opportunists submitted bids of $10,000 and $12,000. Finally, I hired one whose price was $5,750. He proved to be conscientious and skillful, but worked at a slow pace. As this was to be my own residence and I needed time to sell my present home, his slow pace did not bother me.

Initially, it is important to get many bids in every category. However, do not make this a regular practice. After a while, some firms will refuse to bid because they have never received any contracts. If you want to receive good service and be assured of quality work, the best strategy is to develop ongoing contacts with two or three subs and suppliers in each category.

Usually the smallest crews—one or two workers—are able to complete the work most efficiently in the least labor hours overall. This is especially true in carpentry, mechanicals, drywall, insulation, and painting. In concrete or masonry work, however, this is not always true. Subs with the optimum crew composition can afford to offer lower bids. Don't waste time soliciting bids from subs who have plenty of work far into the future. They will tend to give very high bids or no bid at all.

Be sure to look professional and established, even if you are just starting out. Use letterhead for bid instructions, a business name, business cards, and business checks. This will give subcontractors the impression that you are stable and that there will be repeat business.

See Figures 6.1, 6.2, and 6.3 for examples of requests for bids.

Case Study:
An Extreme Case of Getting Multiple Bids

During the 1960s, a professor of business in Illinois purposely solicited 30 to 40 proposals from contractors for an addition to his home. He analyzed the proposals and placed them into categories such as: one-person carpenter operations; larger contractors with hourly crews; and general contractors who sublet everything and were mainly engaged in sales and

John Doe Builders

1234 Success Road, Anywhere, USA (123) 456-7890

New Home: 566 Happy Drive, Anywhere. Lot 1, Block 2, Valley View Subdivision.

FOUNDATION SPECIFICATIONS AND REQUEST FOR BID

Work to include, per plans:

· Basement and garage wall footings: <u>210 lineal feet</u>, concrete needed: <u>9 cubic yards</u>

· Column footings (24" x 24" x 12"): <u>5 each</u>
· 8' high x 8" thick basement walls, or reinforced concrete: <u>138 lineal feet</u>
· 4' high x 6" thick garage foundation walls, of non-reinforced concrete: <u>72 lineal feet</u>
  Concrete needed for above three items: <u>33 cubic yards</u>. Rebar needed: <u>300 feet of 1/2"</u>.

Wall work to include:
· Basement drain tile and stone cover: <u>138 lineal feet</u>
· Asphalt dampproofing: <u>966 square feet</u>
· Basement haunches: <u>2</u>
· Basement windows, including storm and screen: <u>3</u>
· Anchor bolts: <u>per code</u>
· Beam pockets: <u>2</u>

Note: The above list of quantities is deemed complete and very accurate, but checking them over before bidding is your responsibility.

Please do not include the following items in bid:
    · Steel beam and posts
    · Basement window wells
    · Basement floor and other concrete flatwork
You may furnish separate prices on each of these three items, if you wish.

Thank you.

Figure 6.1 Sample Request for Bids for Foundation Work

John Doe Builders

1234 Success Road, Anywhere, USA (123) 456-7890

New Home: 566 Happy Drive, Anywhere. Lot 1, Block 2, Valley View Subdivision.

HEATING SPECIFICATIONS AND REQUEST FOR BID

· Gutters: White enameled steel. Box: <u>118 lineal feet</u>. Rectangular downspouts: <u>6, each 56 lineal feet.</u>

· Flashing: Valleys: <u>2 sets.</u> Tin shingles, chimney chase cover. (Fireplace, firestop, and flue by others.)

· Vents: Furnace vent and conventional vent gas hot water heater. No clothes chute. Bath fans: <u>3</u>. Kitchen hood fan. Clothes dryer vent. Check location of furnace and hot water heater vents.

· Heating: "Magic Heat Hi-E" model: 80,000 Btu, natural gas furnace. No humidifier, Hi-Lo CA returns. List number of WA and CA on bid.

Note: The above list of quantities is deemed complete and very accurate, but checking them over before bidding is your responsibility.

Alternates: Central air; hanging furnace for temporary heat in winter.

Please furnish separate prices on each of the alternates.

Thank you.

Figure 6.2 Sample Request for Bids for Heating Work

John Doe Builders

1234 Success Road, Anywhere, USA (123) 456-7890

New Home: 566 Happy Drive, Anywhere. Lot 1, Block 2, Valley View Subdivision.

ROUGH CARPENTRY/FRAMING WORK ITEMS AND REQUEST FOR BID

Work to include, per plans (labor and nails only):

· Basement mudsill/plate, with sill sealer: <u>138 lineal feet</u>.
· 2" x 10" floor joists with 3/4" O.S.B. plywood floor and bridging: <u>1,964 square feet</u>.
· 8' high, 2" x 4", 16" O.C. exterior house walls with steel wind braces and 1" styrofoam sheathing: <u>284 lineal feet</u>.
· 8' high, 2" x 4", 16" O.C. interior partition walls: <u>348 lineal feet</u>.
· 8' high, 2" x 4", 16" O.C. garage walls with 1/2" comp. sheathing: <u>72 lineal feet</u>.
· Install roof trusses and sheath gable ends: <u>4 each</u>.
    30' span: 18 each – 2nd floor
    16' span: 3 each – 1st floor
    24' span: 11 each – garage

· Sheath all roofs, 1/2" O.S.B. plywood: <u>80</u> 4' x 8' sheets or <u>2,560 square feet</u>.
· Construct 16' wide rafter overlay for valley area.
· Construct porch roof: rafter joists and ceiling: <u>64 square feet</u>.
· 12" wide gable roof overhangs with soffits: <u>132 lineal feet</u>.
· 24" wide level roof overhangs with soffits: <u>108 lineal feet</u>.
· Construct fireplace chimney chase, outside wall.
· Construct upper stairs per plan.
· Drop ceilings, stiff backs, and miscellaneous.
· Install <u>sixteen (16)</u> window units.
· Install <u>one (1)</u> sliding glass door units.
· Install <u>three (3)</u> pre-hung entry doors.
· Install <u>five (5)</u> 4" x 6" cedar corner boards: <u>135 feet of corner</u>.
· Install chimney chase crown.
· Set shower and tub fiberglass modules inside bathroom areas.

Note: The above list of quantities is deemed complete and very accurate, but checking them over before bidding is your responsibility.

Figure 6.3 Sample Request for Bids for Rough Carpentry/FramingWork

Construction adhesives and rough hardware, except nails, furnished by builder. No temporary electric at job site – bring your generator. A very complete and detailed lumber list will be furnished to the Head Carpenter. Builder agrees not to hold up work progress for lack of material, without compensation to carpenter sub.

Please do not include the following items in the above bid:
· Siding work
· Interior millwork and finish/trim carpentry.
You may furnish separate prices on each of these items, if you wish.

Thank you.

Figure 6.3 Sample Request for Bids for Rough Carpentry/FramingWork (cont'd)

expediting. He found a great variance in price. In general—but only in general—the smaller operators had lower bids. His studies were published in a magazine.

Using More Subcontractors and Suppliers

The strategy of saving money by hiring more subs and using more suppliers involves writing more checks for each home than the average builder would, and certainly more than larger builders do. By breaking down the subcontracted jobs and sources for materials into more parts, it is possible to lower overall construction costs. In this way, you can get an edge over other small builders and also compete with your largest competitors whose so-called "economies of scale" are assumed to be in their favor.

Here are some cases in which I have used this strategy.

Case Study:
Hiring More Subs for Concrete and Masonry Work

On many homes that I have built, I have not given concrete flatwork to the foundation/basement sub, because I know he often subcontracts the flatwork to a specialist who is more efficient than his own crews. He also adds a markup to the flatwork contractor's price to cover his expediting time and responsibility. In this way, I save the foundation contractor's markup and gain more control of the flatwork operation. A small amount of extra time on the builder's part can result in the removal of a layer of profit (the foundation sub's markup on flatwork resublet). This is the essence of "disintermediation."

Case Study:
Obtaining Multiple Subs for the Same Job

In general, I ask rough/framing carpentry subs to bid framing only. Any finish carpentry work that they wish to bid is furnished as a separate figure. I ask plumbers not to include a well pump, sewer/water hookup, lateral or septic system in the house plumbing bid—they are all bid separately. Gathering these separate bids and working with more subs and suppliers requires extra time, but the rewards make it very worthwhile. Specialists who offer extreme specialization (such as a carpenter who only installs underlayment flooring) offer increased labor productivity—often 20 percent or more. Consequently, bids from a specialist can be lower than others.

Of course, if this approach is carried too far, a point of diminishing returns is reached. Be sure the additional time spent at purchasing and expediting more subs and suppliers returns enough money to make it worthwhile.

Eliminating Layers of Profit

To bring a product to market at the lowest possible cost, layers of profit must be eliminated. This requires reducing as many intermediary firms and their profits as possible. For example, I often use vinyl sheet flooring made by a popular nationwide manufacturer. I can't buy the vinyl from the manufacturer directly, but I save by buying from their largest direct customer, a chain tile store. Another example is that carpet can now be purchased directly from mills in Georgia. More and more, it is possible to deal direct or almost direct.

Case Study:
Extreme Division of Subcontractor Work

I once saved 20 to 30 percent off the normal masonry contractor's cost for a total masonry fireplace. The foundation and ash pit were built by the foundation contractor. A temporary spring limit on heavy trucking prevented delivery of the fireplace rough materials from our normal supplier, so I laid one course of concrete block and brought in enough concrete myself to pour a sub-hearth. Using a rented truck, I delivered the remaining rough materials because spring road weight limits prevented delivery by the supplier. Two masons agreed to rough up the structure and lay brick on the short roof chimney over a weekend for $400. Later, an individual masonry contractor installed stone facing to the future mantle using stone I had picked up. That degree of subdividing work tasks on a fireplace or similar job can be quite a bother, but it worked out fine in this instance.

The List of Lists

Having a complete set of lists for all the materials that go into a home will allow for more control and make it easy to shop for materials. Accurate material lists will enable subs to come up with tight, accurate bids that are easier to check.

Starting from the beginning of construction, the lists may include:

- Excavation: Yards of earth in an average 6′ deep basement excavation plus lineal feet of trench work for garage foundation.
- Foundation: Lineal feet of wall footings; numbers of column footings; type and number of concrete blocks, mortar and sand, or lineal feet of 8′ high and 4′ high poured concrete foundation walls; volume of concrete in footings and walls; basement windows; length of exterior foundation drain lines; asphalt coating area; rigid foundation insulation area.
- Structural steel: Size and length of beams; number of columns.
- Lumber-rough: A detailed discussion of this follows later in this chapter.
- Roof trusses.
- Window list.
- Exterior door list.
- Roofing: Squares of roofing; rolls of felt; pounds of nails; number of roof vents.
- Insulation: Square footage areas and types/thicknesses of wall, floor and ceiling insulation.
- Drywall: Area of 1/2″ and 5/8″ sheetrock. A good rule is to multiply the total floor area of the home by 3.7, then add the area of garage firewall. Check estimates against the drywall contractor's supply invoice and deduct any returned sheets.
- Concrete flatwork: Separate areas of various kinds of floors, porches and also lineal feet of steps and door sills. Also, list the quantities of materials used.
- Siding list: Materials needed, including waste and nails. An accurate summation of the net wall area covered is required. Then calculate the

average overlap if it is lap siding, add for waste and also extra waste up in gable ends. I have achieved close accuracy using an overall factor of 1.42 for beveled 8″ cedar siding and a factor of 1.3 for 8″ manufactured lap sidings. Multiply these factors times the net wall area. For aluminum siding, try 1.05–1.08.

- Underlayment flooring: For under vinyl and ceramic floors.
- Cabinet list: Box by box list.
- Final lumber: Basement stair parts; finish porch parts; and rough mantle frame.
- Interior doors and trim list: Base, casing, closet shelves, etc.
- Upper stair parts: Rail, balusters, newels.
- Special interior trim: Oak boards for wall caps, mantle, crown molding, etc.
- Light fixtures: By location.
- Finish hardware list; interior glass: shower door, mirrors.
- Floor coverings: Yardage of carpeting, linoleum; square footage of ceramic tile.
- Finish masonry: Exterior veneers square footage, interior fireplace facing.
- Painting: Areas of surfaces—interior, exterior; gallons of various paints, stains, and varnish.

These lists may not be complete during the first project; they may have to be accumulated over the course of a number of projects. Figure 6.4 shows three sample lists: for interior doors and trim; for secondary interior and finish lumber; and for cabinets and finish hardware.

When your lists are complete, keep them in a binder or in a computer file. Not only are these lists useful for ordering materials and checking bids, but they also are easy to revise for a new house plan.

Drawings and Notations

Some builders furnish very little information to bidders, possibly hoping that errors will be made in their favor. This can lead to problems. It is better to furnish lists, plan notations, and other items that make it easy for subs to bid and execute the work. Don't "talk down" to bidders or give them the impression that you are difficult to please. Invite them to check over quantities for themselves. When awarding a subcontract based on a phone bid received on the same day, be sure to discuss the quantities that the bid was based on.

Mark the diagonal lengths needed to square up the building on the plan with red pencil. Circle items, dimensions, or instructions that need special attention. The same procedure applies to the framing contractor. Both the framing and foundation subs' work are performed by people with great physical strength who generally spend little time at a desk going over the plan before they begin. With a red pencil, remind the carpenter of notes on stairwell dimensions, odd rough openings, separated double joists where soil stacks go through, and the dimensioning system. Anything unusual should be called out in red pencil. An attached list of window rough openings or the window catalog will help, should the windows arrive late.

Means Forms

| QUANTITY SHEET | INTERIOR DOORS & TRIM LIST – PRIMARY | | SHEET NO. 1 OF 1 |

PROJECT SINGLE FAMILY SPEC – "VERNON #2" DESIGN
ESTIMATE NO.

LOCATION LOT 20, HAPPY HOLLOW **ARCHITECT** **DATE**

TAKEOFF BY JOHN DOE BUILDER **EXTENSIONS BY** **CHECKED BY**

DESCRIPTION	NO.	DIMENSIONS	UNIT		UNIT		UNIT	
PRE-HUNG DOORS: 4 3/8" OAK VENEER JAMBS, COLONIAL OAK STOPS, 2 1/4" OAK CASINGS, FLUSH OAK H.C. DOORS –								
	2 –	2/8 HINGE LEFT						
	4 –	2/8 HINGE RIGHT (FIR CASING ONE SIDE OF ONE DOOR)						
	1 –	2/6 HINGE RIGHT						
	1 –	2/4 HINGE RIGHT (ONE FIR CASING SIDE)						
	1 –	2/2 HINGE LEFT (ONE FIR CASING SIDE)						
	1 –	2/2 HINGE RIGHT (ONE FIR CASING SIDE)						
	1 –	2/0 HINGE RIGHT (ONE FIR CASING SIDE)						
	1 –	1/6 HINGE LEFT (ONE FIR CASING SIDE)						
	1 –	3/0 B/F ——— (ONE FIR CASING SIDE)						
SLIDING CLOSET DOORS: H.C. FLUSH OAK DOORS, TRACK, OAK VENEER JAMBS, 2 1/4" OAK COLONIAL CASINGS OUTSIDE, FIR CASINGS INSIDE								
	2 –	6/0 OPENINGS, USING 3/0 DOORS						
PLUS 2 1/4" COLONIAL OAK CASINGS FOR THE FOLLOWING WINDOWS (D.H.) & DOORS:								
	2 –	24/24 MULL UNITS						
	1 –	28/28 SINGLE						
	1 –	30/28 SINGLE						
D.H.	1 –	32/24 SINGLE						
	3 –	28/24 SINGLE						
	3 –	20/24 SINGLE						
	1 –	6/24 SINGLE						
	1 –	24/36 SLIDER, SINGLE						
	1 –	3/0 ENTRY DOOR						
	1 –	2/8 ENTRY DOOR						
	1 –	6/0 PATIO DOOR						
	2 –	OCTAGON WINDOWS @ 12" PER SIDE						
	36'	OF CASING FOR UNDER WALL CAPS						
BASE AND SHOE:	420' –	2 3/8" OAK, RANCH BASE						
	100' –	2 1/4" FIR, RANCH BASE						
	30' –	OAK SHOE						
STAIR PARTS:	2 –	16' OAK VENEER STAIR SKIRTS						
	1 –	14' ROUND PINE HANDRAIL						
CLOSET PARTS:	5 –	12' PIECES SHELF CLEAT						
	4 –	16' PCS. HOOK STRIP						
	3 –	12' PCS. CLOSET POLE						
	6 –	12' PCS. – 12" WHITE SHELF						
	2 –	16' PCS. – 16" WHITE SHELF						
MULL STRIPS:	4 –	6' PCS. – 1 3/4" OAK						

Figure 6.4 Sample Quantity Sheets

⚖ Means Forms

QUANTITY SHEET   SECONDARY INTERIOR & FINISH LUMBER LIST

PROJECT SINGLE FAMILY SPEC — "VERNON #2" DESIGN   ESTIMATE NO.

LOCATION LOT 20, HAPPY HOLLOW   ARCHITECT   DATE

TAKEOFF BY JOHN DOE BUILDER   EXTENSIONS BY   CHECKED BY

DESCRIPTION	NO.	DIMENSIONS		UNIT		UNIT		UNIT
STAIR PARTS:	14'	OF RAIL, HEMLOCK, #610 "SOUTHPORT"						
	1 –	48" NEWEL POST, HEMLOCK, "NEW HAMPTON"						
	25 –	31" BALUSTERS, HEMLOCK, "SOUTHPORT"						
OAK BOARDS:	3 –	1" x 8" – 16' MANTLE TOP, APRON & WALL CAPS						
	1 –	1" x 10" – 12' ARCH BOARD & WALL CAP						
	1 –	9' OAK CROWN MOLDING, UNDER MANTLE TOP						
FLOOR UNDERLAYMENT:	15 –	4' x 8' – 1/4" LUAN PLYWOOD UNDERLAYMENT - TOP GRADE						
	1 –	ROLL – 15# FELT						
FINISH LUMBER:	2 –	2" x 12" – 14' DOUGLAS FIR BASEMENT STAIR STRINGERS						
	1 –	2" x 4" – 8' OUTDOOR WOOD						
	8 –	2" x 4" – 8' STUDS						
	3 –	1" x 8" – 14' #2 PINE RISERS						
	1 –	1" x 8" – 8' #2 PINE RISERS						
	3 –	5/4" x 12" – 14' SYP STAIR TREAD						
	1 –	5/4" x 12" – 8' SYP STAIR TREAD						
	190	L.F. – 1" x 8" V-GROOVE K.P. PANELING						
	2 –	4" x 4" – 8' OUTDOOR WOOD POSTS						
	2 –	1" x 6" – 16' #2 PINE POST COVERS						
	2 –	1" x 8" – 16' #2 PINE POST COVERS						
	2 –	1" x 12" – 10' #2 PINE CURVE BOARDS						

Figure 6.4 Sample Quantity Sheets (cont'd)

⚓ Means Forms

QUANTITY SHEET CABINET LIST & FINISH HARDWARE LIST										SHEET NO. 1 OF 1	

PROJECT _SINGLE FAMILY SPEC - "VERNON #2" DESIGN_   ESTIMATE NO.

LOCATION _LOT 20, HAPPY HOLLOW_   ARCHITECT   DATE

TAKEOFF BY _JOHN DOE BUILDER_   EXTENSIONS BY   CHECKED BY

DESCRIPTION	NO.	DIMENSIONS			UNIT				UNIT				UNIT			
KITCHEN — ALL "ULTRA"	1 —	B39														
	1 —	BD21														
	1 —	45/48 BBC, INCL. 1" FILLER & TDF3 FILLER														
	1 —	B12L														
	1 —	SB 36														
	1 —	18 R														
	1 —	2130L														
	1 —	3018														
	1 —	2430R														
	1 —	2430 WC-L														
	1 —	6' VAL														
	1 —	3030														
BATHS — ALL "TRADITIONAL"	1 —	VBD - 58														
	1 —	VBS - 30 - 18" DEEP														
	1 —	VBDS - 36 - 18" DEEP														
FINISH HARDWARE LIST																
LOCKSET — "MEGA"	3 —	ENTRY, W/ DRIVE BOLTS, KEYED ALIKE														
U.S. 5 FINISH	7 —	PRIVACY, W/ DRIVE BOLTS														
U.S. 5 FINISH	5 —	PASSAGE, W/ DRIVE BOLTS														
DOOR PULLS	1 —	FOR B/F DOOR														
DOOR PULLS	2 PR. —	FOR SLIDE-BY DOORS, LARGE DIA.														
DOOR STOPS	11 —	SPRING TYPE, 2 PART														
HANDRAIL BRACKETS	2 PR.															
CLOSET SHELF BRACKETS	6 —	EA.														
CLOSET POLE HOLDERS	7 PR.															

Figure 6.4 Sample Quantity Sheets (cont'd)

Lumber and Millwork Lists

There are at least three options for producing a lumber list to present to suppliers who are bidding the work: using a lumber listing service; creating your own list; or first using a service and from that, learning to create your own list. The rough lumber list example shown in Figure 6.5 can be helpful in compiling your own list.

Don't let lumber dealers bid based on a list they compile from your plans. Each of them will probably come up with slightly different quantities. In some parts of the country, there are services that will provide a list of all the rough lumber needed to complete your plan. For a cost of several hundred dollars, a lumber listing service will create a thorough, accurate list of pieces that also reflects local carpentry construction practices. Individual carpenters will differ in the way they frame roof overhangs, for example. Your list should reflect the practices of your most likely carpenter sub and these practices should be the most efficient. I was fortunate to have learned of a lumber listing service early in my career. The lister I used had decades of experience at lumber yards. He specified the most practical species and grades of lumber for everything on the list and also recommended that the six copies of the list be used to obtain six lumber bids. Framing lumber is usually the largest dollar cost component item in the home.

One of the main advantages of submitting a prepared list for bids is that each supplier will be pricing the same quantities – so that when you receive bids from different suppliers, you'll be comparing apples with apples. You will still need to determine that each supplier's bid list exactly matches the original list, and you may need to satisfy yourself as to the quality of the suppliers' stock.

To facilitate the bidding process and reduce errors in the bid list, you might reduce the construction lumber list to a consolidated list. The 2″ x 4″–16′ will appear only once on this list, for example. See Figure 6.6 for an example.

If you obtain lumber bids from plans without providing suppliers with your own list, you are doing what many small builders do: risking confusing bids, and adding to the supplier's workload. Every lumber supplier has at least one employee – usually overworked – who will create a lumber list from your plans. There will almost certainly be errors. The supplier with the list that errs on the short side may come up the lowest price, but you will eventually need more lumber to finish your project and these missing pieces might be priced at the higher "casual purchase" contractor rate.

Don't confuse your framing lumber bid by allowing the lumber dealer to include roof trusses, siding, exterior doors, roofing, sheetrock, interior doors/millwork, or cabinet prices in with the lumber bid. Keep every category separate. When building one home, I went so far as to purchase only the plywood CDX sheathing from a special dealer to save some money.

You can use an additional resource such as *Means Estimating Handbook* to create lists. See the Resources Appendix for more information about this handbook.

By compiling your own lumber list, you will have a better feel for value engineering applications and have better control of the entire business. Learning this process is worth the effort. If you don't have the time, hire a good, independent lister for this quantity surveying specialty.

QUANTITY SHEET <u>ROUGH LUMBER LIST</u>   SHEET NO. **1 OF 3**

PROJECT **SINGLE FAMILY SPEC — "STRATFORD" DESIGN**   ESTIMATE NO.

LOCATION **LOT 20, HAPPY HOLLOW**   ARCHITECT   DATE

TAKEOFF BY **JOHN DOE BUILDER**   EXTENSIONS BY   CHECKED BY

DESCRIPTION	NO.	DIMENSIONS		UNIT	UNIT	UNIT
FOAM SILL SEALER	200'	OF 4"				
1st FL. RIM JOISTS	6 –	2"x10"–14'	STD. & BTR. DOUG. FIR			
1st FL. JOISTS	27 –	2"x10"–16'	STD. & BTR. DOUG. FIR			
1st FL. JOISTS	33 –	2"x10"–14'	STD. & BTR. DOUG. FIR			
1st FL. JOISTS	8 –	2"x10"–12'	STD. & BTR. DOUG. FIR			
ALL BRIDGING	320'	OF 1"x3"	ROUGH			
ALL JOIST HANGERS	22 –	2"x10"–12"	SINGLES			
ALL JOIST HANGERS	6 –	2"x10"–12"	DOUBLES			
ALL FLOOR GLUE	20 –	1 QUART TUBES "PL400"				
1st FL. FLOORING	36 –	4'x8'–3/4"	T&G O.S.B. ("OXBOARD" OR EQUAL) UNSANDED			
1st FL. EXT. WALL PLATES	30 –	2"x4"–16'	STD. & BTR. HEM-FIR			
1st FL. EXT. WALL STUDS	180 –	2"x4"–92 5/8"	STD. & BTR. HEM-FIR			
1st FL. EXT. WALL HEADERS	2 –	2"x12"–14'	STD. & BTR. DOUG. FIR (BOX BAY & PATIO DOOR)			
1st FL. EXT. WALL HEADERS	2 –	2"x12"–12'	STD. & BTR. DOUG. FIR (DINING & FAMILY MULLS)			
1st FL. EXT. WALL HEADERS	2 –	2"x8"–14'	STD. & BTR. DOUG. FIR (ENTRY DOOR + 28' D.H.)			
1st. FL. EXT. WALL HEADERS	1 –	2"x8"–16'	STD. & BTR. DOUG. FIR (FIREPLACE & FOYER CAS.)			
1st FL. EXT. WALL HEADERS	1 –	2"x8"–12'	STD. & BTR. DOUG. FIR (FIRE DOOR & LAUNDRY)			
ALL LET-IN BRACES	30 –	1"x4"–10'	COM. PINE OR SPRUCE			
1st FL. WALL SHEATH.	33 –	4'x8'–1"	STYROFOAM ("DOW" OR "FORMULA 250")			
1st FL. WALL SHEATH.	7 –	4'x8'–1/2"	COMPOSITION (FOR GARAGE FIREWALL)			
BOX BAY WINDOW	5 –	2"x6"–12'	STD. & BTR. HEM-FIR (RAFTERS & HEADER)			
BOX BAY WINDOW	1 –	4'x8'–1/2"	O.S.B. (BAY ROOF)			
1st FL. INT. WALL PLATES	24 –	2"x4"–16'	STD. & BTR. HEM-FIR			
1st FL. INT. WALL PLATES	3 –	2"x6"–12'	STD. & BTR. HEM-FIR			
1st FL. INT. WALL STUDS	140 –	2"x4"–92 5/8"	STD. & BTR. HEM-FIR			
1st FL. INT. WALL STUDS	10 –	2"x6"–92 5/8"	STD. & BTR. HEM-FIR			
1st FL. INT. WALL HEADERS	1 –	2"x12"–14'	STD. & BTR. DOUG. FIR (LIV. – FAM. RM)			
1st FL. INT. WALL HEADERS	3 –	4"x4"–16'	STD. & BTR. DOUG. FIR			
2nd FL. BEAM	2 –	2"x10"–12'	STD. & BTR. DOUG. FIR			
2nd FL. RIM JOISTS	2 –	2"x10"–16'	STD. & BTR. DOUG. FIR			
2nd FL. RIM JOISTS	2 –	2"x10"–18'	STD. & BTR. DOUG. FIR			
2nd FL. JOISTS	13 –	2"x10"–18'	STD. & BTR. DOUG. FIR			
2nd FL. JOISTS	38 –	2"x10"–14"	STD. & BTR. DOUG. FIR			
2nd FL. JOISTS	3 –	2"x10"–12'	STD. & BTR. DOUG. FIR			
2nd FL. FLOORING	30 –	4'x8'–3/4"	T&G O.S.B. ("OXBOARD" OR EQUAL)			
2nd FL. EXT. WALL PLATES	26 –	2"x4"–16'	STD. & BTR. HEM-FIR			
2nd FL. EXT. WALL STUDS	160 –	2"x4"–92 5/8"	STD. & BTR. HEM-FIR			
2nd FL. EXT. WALL HEADERS	5 –	2"x12"–14'	STD. & BTR. DOUG. FIR (MULL. WINDOW & BED. #3 BEAM)			
2nd FL. EXT. WALL HEADERS	3 –	2"x8"–12'	STD. & BTR. DOUG. FIR			
2nd FL. EXT. WALL SHEATH.	33 –	4'x8'–1"	STYROFOAM ("DOW" OR "FORMULA 250")			
TRIM FOR BOX BAYS	1 –	4'x8'–3/8"	SAW TEX. EXT. FIR PLYWOOD			
TRIM FOR BOX BAYS	1 –	1"x12"–8'	RUF CEDAR			

Figure 6.5 Sample Quantity Sheets

Means Forms

QUANTITY SHEET <u>ROUGH LUMBER LIST</u>

PROJECT <u>SINGLE FAMILY SPEC — "STRATFORD" DESIGN</u>

ESTIMATE NO.

LOCATION <u>LOT 20, HAPPY HOLLOW</u>   ARCHITECT

DATE

TAKEOFF BY <u>JOHN DOE BUILDER</u>   EXTENSIONS BY

CHECKED BY

DESCRIPTION	NO.	DIMENSIONS	UNIT		UNIT		UNIT	
TRIM FOR BOX BAYS	4 –	1" x 8" – 16' RUF CEDAR						
CHIMNEY STUDS/PLATES	15 –	2" x 4" – 92 5/8" STD. & BTR. HEM-FIR						
CHIMNEY STUDS/PLATES	17 –	2" x 4" – 10' STD & BTR. HEM-FIR						
CHIMNEY SHEATHING	8 –	4' x 8' – 1/2" O.S.B.						
CHIMNEY CROWN	1 –	2" x 10" – 16' RUF CEDAR						
GABLE SHEATHING	11 –	4' x 8' – 25/32" COMPOSITION						
GABLE SOFFIT NAILERS	8 –	2" x 6" – 18' STD. & BTR. HEM-FIR						
GABLE SOFFIT NAILERS	8 –	2" x 6" – 16' STD. & BTR. HEM-FIR (FOR GARAGE)						
GABLE FASCIA	9 –	1" x 8" – 16' #2 & BTR. PINE (INC. GARAGE)						
GABLE SOFFIT	10 –	1' x 8' – 3/8" AC EXT. FIR PLYWOOD (INC GARAGE)						
GABLE RAKE MOLD.	10 –	1" x 2" – 14' #2 & BTR. PINE (INC GARAGE)						
SOFFIT NAILER	11 –	1" x 4" – 12' COMMON PINE OR SPRUCE (INC. GARAGE)						
SOFFIT LOOKOUTS	12 –	2" x 4" – 12' STD & BTR. HEM-FIR (INC. GARAGE)						
SUB-FASCIA	13 –	1" x 6" – 12' COMMON PINE OR SPRUCE (INC. GARAGE & PORCH)						
FASCIA	13 –	1" x 8" – 12' #2 & BTR. PINE (INC. GARAGE & PORCH)						
SOFFIT	9 –	4' x 8' – 3/8" AC EXT. FIR PLYWOOD (INC GARAGE & PORCH)						
GARAGE PLATES	14 –	2" x 4" – 16' STD. & BTR. HEM-FIR						
GARAGE STUDS	70 –	2" x 4" – 92 5/8" STD & BTR. HEM-FIR						
GARAGE HEADERS	1 –	2" x 8" – 18' STD. & BTR. DOUG. FIR (WINDOWS & SERVICE DOOR)						
OVERHEAD DOOR HEADERS	3 –	2" x 12" – 18' STD. & BTR. DOUG. FIR						
OVERHEAD DOOR JAMB	1 –	1" x 6' – 16' #2 & BTR. PINE						
OVERHEAD DOOR JAMB	1 –	1" x 6' – 14' #2 & BTR. PINE						
OVERHEAD DOOR BRICK MOLD.	30'	(1 – 16' + 1 – 14') PINE						
2nd FL. INT. WALL PLATES	25 –	2" x 4" – 16' STD. & BTR. HEM-FIR						
2nd FL. INT. WALL PLATES	3 –	2" x 6" – 10' STD & BTR. HEM-FIR						
2nd FL. INT. WALL STUDS	10 –	2" x 6" – 92 5/8" STD. & BTR. HEM-FIR						
2nd FL. INT. WALL STUDS	152 –	2" x 4" – 92 5/8" STD. & BTR. HEM-FIR						
2nd FL. INT. WALL HEADERS	2 –	4" x 4" – 16' STD. & BTR. DOUG. FIR						
FRONT GABLE RAFTERS	8 –	2" x 6" – 12' STD. & BTR. HEM-FIR						
FRONT GABLE CEILING JOISTS	3 –	2" x 6" – 10' STD. & BTR. HEM-FIR						
PORCH RAFTERS & CEILING JOISTS	15 –	2" x 4" – 10' STD. & BTR. HEM-FIR						
PORCH RAFTER NAILER	2 –	2" x 6" – 10' STD. & BTR. HEM-FIR						
GARAGE ROOF NAILER	3 –	2" x 6" – 16' STD. & BTR. HEM-FIR						
LAUNDRY CEILING JOISTS	5 –	2" x 6" – 12' STD. & BTR. HEM-FIR						
LAUNDRY RAFTERS	10 –	2" x 6" – 10' STD. & BTR. HEM-FIR						
LAUNDRY RIDGE RAFTERS	1 –	2" x 8" – 14' STD. & BTR. DOUG. FIR						
RIDGE BOARD & OVERLAY	6 –	1" x 8" – 12' COMMON PINE OR SPRUCE						
FOYER CEILING JOISTS	3 –	2" x 8" – 18' STD. & BTR. DOUG. FIR						
FOYER CEILING NAILER	2 –	2" x 4" – 16' STD. & BTR. HEM-FIR						
TRUSS STIFF BACKS	15 –	2" x 4" – 14' STD. & BTR. HEM-FIR (INCL. DROP CEILING)						

Figure 6.5 Sample Quantity Sheets (cont'd)

Means Forms

QUANTITY SHEET ROUGH LUMBER LIST

SHEET NO. **3 OF 3**

PROJECT SINGLE FAMILY SPEC — "STRATFORD" DESIGN

ESTIMATE NO.

LOCATION LOT 20, HAPPY HOLLOW   **ARCHITECT**

DATE

TAKEOFF BY JOHN DOE BUILDER   **EXTENSIONS BY**

CHECKED BY

DESCRIPTION	NO.	DIMENSIONS		UNIT	UNIT	UNIT
CEILING BACKER	6 —	2"x10"— 12'	STD. & BTR. HEM-FIR			
ROOF SHEATHING	81 —	4'x8'— ½"	O.S.B. ("OXBOARD" OR EQUAL) UNSANDED			
PLY CLIPS	250	EA. FOR ½" PLY.				
ALL SOFFIT VENTS	8	EA. — 8"x16" METAL				
— END OF FRAMING LIST —						
↳ SEPARATE PRICE: OUTSIDE TRIM ↲						
CORNER BOARDS	2 —	5/4"x10"— 18'	RUF CEDAR (RIP AT LUMBER YARD TO 5¼" & 4½")			
CORNER BOARDS	3 —	5/4"x10"— 16'	RUF CEDAR (RIP AT LUMBER YARD TO 5¼" & 4½")			
CORNER BOARDS	5 —	5/4"x10"— 14'	RUF CEDAR (RIP AT LUMBER YARD TO 5¼" & 4½")			
WINDOW SILL TRIM	4 —	2"x10"— 12'	RUF CEDAR			
APPLIQUE STOCK	2 —	1"x8"— 12'	RUF CEDAR			
PORCH COLUMN	1 —	4"x6"— 8'	SMOOTH FIR			
PORCH CURVE BOARDS	2 —	1"x12"— 10'	#2 & BTR. PINE			

Figure 6.5 Sample Quantity Sheets (cont'd)

94

⚖ Means Forms

QUANTITY SHEET <u>CONSOLIDATED ROUGH LUMBER BID LIST</u>

PROJECT **SINGLE FAMILY SPEC — "BRADFORD" DESIGN**   ESTIMATE NO.

LOCATION **LOT 29, HAPPY HOLLOW**   ARCHITECT   DATE

TAKEOFF BY **JOHN DOE BUILDER**   EXTENSIONS BY   CHECKED BY

DESCRIPTION	NO.	DIMENSIONS		UNIT	UNIT	UNIT
SILL SEALER	150'	OF 4"		BETTER QUALITY IF AVAILABLE		
ALL FLOOR GLUE	22 -	1 QUART TUBES OF "PL400" OR EQUAL				
ALL JOISTS, STAIR	13 -	2" x 10" - 18'		STD & BTR. DOUG. FIR		
STRINGS, DROPS	37 -	2" x 10" - 16'		STD & BTR. DOUG. FIR		
BEAMS	28 -	2" x 10" - 14'		STD & BTR. DOUG. FIR		
	23 -	2" x 10" - 12'		STD & BTR. DOUG. FIR		
↓	42 -	2" x 10" - 10'		STD & BTR. DOUG. FIR		
ALL BRIDGING	275'	OF 1" x 3"		ROUGH FIR		
ALL JOIST HANGERS	20 -	SINGLES FOR 2" x 10"				
ALL JOIST HANGERS	8 -	DOUBLES FOR 2" x 10"				
ALL FLOORING	60 -	4' x 8' - 3/4"		T.& G. O.S.B. ("OXBOARD" OR EQUAL)		
ALL WIND BRACES	32 -	1" x 4" - 12'		COMMON PINE OR SPRUCE		
ALL PLATES & MISC.	126 -	2" x 4" - 16'		STD. & BTR. HEM-FIR		
2 x 4's	2 -	2" x 4" - 14'		STD. & BTR. HEM-FIR		
	33 -	2" x 4" - 12'		STD. & BTR. HEM-FIR		
↓	13 -	2" x 4" - 10'		STD. & BTR. HEM-FIR		
ALL STUDS	635 -	2" x 4" - 92⅝"		STD. & BTR. HEM-FIR PRECUTS		
ALL HEADERS	3 -	2" x 14" - 18'		STD. & BTR. DOUG. FIR		
& TREADS	2 -	2" x 14" - 12'		STD. & BTR. DOUG. FIR		
	1 -	2" x 12" - 16'		STD. & BTR. DOUG. FIR		
	1 -	2" x 12" - 14'		STD. & BTR. DOUG. FIR		
	2 -	2" x 12" - 12'		STD. & BTR. DOUG. FIR		
	1 -	2" x 8" - 16'		STD. & BTR. DOUG. FIR		
	4 -	2" x 8" - 14'		STD. & BTR. DOUG. FIR		
	5 -	2" x 8" - 12'		STD. & BTR. DOUG. FIR		
	2 -	2" x 8" - 10'		STD. & BTR. DOUG. FIR		
	2 -	4" x 6" - 14'		STD. & BTR. DOUG. FIR		
	2 -	4" x 4" - 16'		STD. & BTR. DOUG. FIR		
↓	2 -	4" x 4" - 14'		STD. & BTR. DOUG. FIR		
WALL SHEATHING	63 -	4' x 8' - 1"		STYROFOAM (GREY "DOW" OR EQUAL)		
WALL SHEATHING	12 -	4' x 8' - ½"		COMPOSITION SHEATHING		
WALL & ROOF SHEATHING	94 -	4' x 8' - ½"		O.S.B "OXBOARD" OR EQUAL)		
"PLY-CLIPS"	200 EA.	FOR ½" PLYWOOD				
MISC. FRAMING	9 -	2" x 6" - 16'		STD. & BTR. HEM-FIR		
	8 -	2" x 6" - 12'		STD. & BTR. HEM-FIR		
	14 -	2" x 2" - 12'		STD. & BTR. HEM-FIR		
	7 -	1" x 6" - 16'		COMMON PINE OR SPRUCE		
	3 -	1" x 6" - 12'		COMMON PINE OR SPRUCE		
↓	40 -	1" x 4" - 12'		COMMON PINE OR SPRUCE		
SOFFIT VENTS	10 EA. -	8" x 16"		METAL (WHITE ONLY)		
FASCIA & RISERS	9 -	1" x 6" - 16'		#2 & BTR. PINE		
FASCIA & RISERS	16 -	1" x 8" - 12'		#2 & BTR. PINE		

Figure 6.6 Sample Consolidated List

⚓ Means Forms

QUANTITY SHEET <u>CONSOLIDATED ROUGH LUMBER BID LIST</u>

PROJECT **SINGLE FAMILY SPEC — "BRADFORD" DESIGN**   ESTIMATE NO.

LOCATION **LOT 29, HAPPY HOLLOW**   ARCHITECT   DATE

TAKEOFF BY **JOHN DOE BUILDER**   EXTENSIONS BY   CHECKED BY

DESCRIPTION	NO.	DIMENSIONS		UNIT		UNIT		UNIT
RAKE MOLDING	13 –	1" x 2" – 12' #2 & BTR. PINE						
SOFFIT	2 –	4' x 8' – 3/8" AC EXT. PLYWOOD						
SOFFIT	37 –	1' x 8' – 3/8" AC EXT. PLYWOOD						
OVERHEAD DOOR JAMB	2 –	1" x 6" – 16' #2 & BTR. PINE						
O'HEAD DOOR BRICK MOLDING	2 –	16' PCS.						
CORNER BOARDS	7 –	2" x 10" – 16' RUF CEDAR (RIP AT LUMBERYARD TO 5 3/8" & 4")						
CORNER BOARDS	2 –	2" x 10" – 10' RUF CEDAR (RIP AT LUMBERYARD TO 5 3/8" & 4")						
CHIMNEY CROWN	1 –	2" x 10" – 14' RUF CEDAR – DON'T RIP						
END OF BID #1 ROUGH LUMBER								
BID #2								
SIDING	2816☐ (33 BUNDLES) (85.33☐ PER BUNDLE) OF 7/16" x 8" PRIMED O.S.B. BODY, RUF GRAIN, "L-P INNER SEAL" OR EQUAL.							
SIDING NAILS	1 –	100# BOX – 16d "MAZE" GALV. SIDING NAILS						

Figure 6.6 Sample Consolidated List (cont'd)

After using a listing service for several homes, I was able to develop my own system. My list begins with sill sealer, then mud sill if required, first-floor rim joists or box sill, regular first-floor joists, special length joists, joist hangers, bridging, plywood flooring, glue, wall plates and studs, headers, and so on. On a 2,000 square foot home, this list can be three or four pages long. Your lead carpenter can save time and waste by referring to this list. For example, if the only 2″ x 4″s–18′ long are to be used for a fireplace, he should not use them as first-floor exterior wall plates. I usually separate interior partition plates from the exterior plates as well as the studs. A good rule of thumb for calculating studs that are 16″ on center is to multiply each lineal foot of wall through all openings, except an overhead garage door, by 1.15. This factor will allow for extra studs used at intersections, shoulder studs, etc.

The most common framing shortages during construction occur in wall plates, studs, and floor joists. Avoid delays, sudden trips to the lumber yard, and the carpenter's anger by having enough material in your list *and* on your site for the expeditious execution of the framing process. If you do your part here, you will find lower carpentry bids and the loyalty of a good, reasonably priced sub. Framing subs tend to avoid builders who have inconvenienced them as soon as business volume allows them that option.

Lumber Lists and Value Engineering

The process of creating a lumber list provides a good opportunity to apply the principles of value engineering. The following are some questions to contemplate when analyzing lumber costs:

- How does the cost of built-up 2″x wood beams compare with glue laminated engineered products?
- Are the outside corners being framed in a way that uses the least number of studs and still provides nailing for siding and sheetrock and ease of insulation?
- Can you find pre-primed roof soffit and fascia materials that are competitive with on-site pre-priming labor?
- How many double joists do you really need?
- Can the drywaller use metal corner clips to save studs and ceiling backer boards?
- Do you really need a mud sill plate?
- What are the options for providing exterior wall wind bracing?
- Compare: 1″ x 4″ let-in; steel straps, sheet plywood, etc. for wind bracing.

When selecting species and grades of lumber, do your homework. In general, I specify standard and better (#1 and #2 construction grades) for joists, plates, studs, and rafters. Joists and wide rafters are Douglas fir, while studs are usually white woods (hem-fir). Number three grades are used for nailers, ceiling backer, etc. Consult with carpenters, lumber yards, and load tables, and check your competitors' work.

Case Study:
An Example of Efficient Roof Overhang Construction

One carpentry sub framed roof soffits and fascias with a long 2″ x 2″, held out from a 1″ x 4″ wall nailer with flat 2″ x 4″ lookouts. The 2″ x 2″

provided nailing for both soffit and fascia and replaced a more expensive 1″ x 4″ or 6″ sub fascia. For gable ends, he used a 1″ x 6″ #3 wall nailer, 2″ x 6″ lookouts, and 2″ x 6″ sub rake. If no gable end overhang was designed, a 2″ x 6″ nailer over the wall sheathing could hold the 1″ x 8″ rake board away from the wall for rain drippage, and provide a hidden 2″ area behind which siding can be fitted with less-than-perfect accuracy in the angle cuts at siding ends.

Your part of the country may use different architecture or framing systems. In my area, "tilt-up" framing, which will be explained in Chapter 8, is used exclusively.

Making Your List

After you have had the experience of building a few homes, it should take about three to four hours to create a lumber list or quantity takeoff for an uncomplicated mid-size home. Remember to incorporate corrections and changes to the list after building each repetition of the original design.

Your interior trim/millwork and door quantity takeoff should take only about an hour. List all interior doors first. I use higher-quality pre-hung units that have hinges, jambs, and stops applied and are bored for locksets and strike plates. From the door list you can list sides of hardwood or softwood casing trim. I use 2-1/4″ colonial detail oak for all room sides and cheaper, smooth-face softwood casings for closet interiors and basements. Don't forget trim sides for doors not on the list: sliding glass doors, front entry doors, and garage entry doors. Keep in mind that pre-hung doors cost only about ten dollars more than their component parts. A finish carpenter cannot hang a door for this cost; you can save a day in the construction cycle by using pre-hung doors.

Window casing lengths can be calculated by your supplier from the window list. Window casings should match door casings. Remember mullion strips.

I use an oak base, but not a tall, detailed one. No one notices this item very closely after carpet is installed, so an expensive base to match the casing exactly is money not wisely spent unless you are building a luxury home. Stair skirts can be oak, oak veneer, or even hemlock or mahogany. Stair railings, balusters, and newels could be oak or hemlock — check costs and the practices of your competitors. Closets and will need closet poles, shelving, hook strips, and cleats. The factory-finished, white particleboard shelves are worth the extra cost.

Items such as stair rail parts, oak wall cap boards, mantle parts, basement stair parts and porch trim can often be purchased less expensively at two or three other suppliers than at the interior door and trim supplier. This is another case in which it pays to use more suppliers.

Your millwork quantity takeoff will get your finish hardware quantity takeoff off to a good start. Select durable, yet economical hardware that looks a little plush.

In general, pre-hung entry doors save money if they are well constructed. I have found that $80 to $100 can buy a well-built, aluminum storm entry door that fits into most exterior schemes, as long as the factory colors can be used. Wood storm doors can be difficult to install and maintain.

Some tools that can help with the takeoff of materials from the plan are a 1/4" scale dial to run along walls to pick up wall lengths, and a joist/rafter rule that shows the number of members needed for 16" or 24" spacings when laid over the plan.

Hiring and Keeping Good Subs and Suppliers

As I have already stated, one of the best ways to find subcontractors and suppliers is to continue to visit sites where other homes are under construction. As months and years go by, some subcontractors go out of business and others start up. Also, new equipment and work methods come into use. Keep abreast of these developments and keep your file of alternate subs and suppliers full and updated.

On the other hand, it is advantageous to stay with your present subs and suppliers as long as it is practical to do so. Each sub has individual business habits and personality characteristics that require time to become acquainted with. Most subs and suppliers will reward your repeat business with better service and personal attention to problems and suggestions. A short list of favored subs and suppliers—at least two for each trade—is what you need.

Negotiating Prices and Work Relationships

"I'm not too bright myself, but I have a lot of bright people working for me." — Anonymous

It is generally easier to attempt negotiation of a lower price with a supplier than with a sub. Some subcontractors are often turned off by behavior that they may consider "chiseling." Experience tells them a chiseler can be both difficult to work with and slow to pay. However, you can benefit from carefully reviewing subcontractor estimates. If you have materials listed and priced, as well as some records of labor-hours required, you will be able to detect a bad estimate or miscalculation by a subcontractor. Point out errors in a very diplomatic way, of course. On the other hand, good subs can often offer suggestions that lower cost, improve design, or raise value.

You may be able to obtain a lower price by giving something in return. Quick payment upon completion, good job conditions, and the offer to do a small, unskilled part of the sub's work are some examples. If you are behind schedule, you may want a financial assurance of prompt work by asking for a discount (as liquidated damages) should the sub not complete work on time, or offering a bonus for early completion.

Sometimes a sub may quote a price on work that is difficult to accurately estimate, with the provision that it could be lower after experiencing the work. A ratio of 25 percent of any savings going to the sub and 75 percent to the builder is a good formula. You should ask the sub to bid the most basic specifications if you are not sure of final choices, since subs often don't give full credit for "downgrading." Explain to each sub all value engineering changes that could provide savings; for example, with your painting sub, discuss pre-primed fascia and soffit materials.

Purchasing materials for the sub may offer overall savings because this removes some risks for the sub. Local practices often dictate whether this is feasible.

Prompt payment brings in lower bids over time—this is an area that is most problematic for subs. Paying your subs weekly, with a one week lag, is one way to ensure good prices and fair treatment. Large-volume builders often are 60 to 75 days late in paying subs, who waive their lien rights on the real estate involved in the first 30 days.

Never tell one sub what one of his or her competitors has bid. This unethical practice of releasing confidential information is known as "bid peddling." Subs who hear of this may refuse to bid more of your work for fear of being pushed into a bidding contest.

Finally, treat subs with respect and consideration. They work long and hard hours. Don't call them at inconvenient times, request endless estimates for changes, get in their way at the job site, and so forth. A sub will drop such a builder as soon as he or she can get along without him.

The Cost Breakdown Sheet

A comprehensive cost breakdown sheet can serve many purposes. It can provide both estimates and final costs for dozens of categories of costs that are arranged to give you the most insight into and control of your business. On one sheet, the total gross profit markup can be broken up into expediting/purchasing/supervision, general overhead, sales expenses, and net profit. From this sheet you can transfer costs to a lender's breakdown sheet, if needed. With an adding machine tape attached, you can determine if overall costs are running ahead of, or behind, estimates during each month of construction. The cost breakdown sheet should be used, if only in a penciled-in "guesstimate" form, when you are selecting a site or a design to determine if the site or design will add up within the overall budget of total costs for the entire package. It is one of the first management tools you will use, as well as the last, when the sale is consummated and you insert all final costs and gross and net profits for future reference.

I use an 8-1/2″ x 14″ sheet with categories listed on both sides, as illustrated in Figure 6.7. I customized the sheet using a lender's construction loan cost breakdown sheet as a model. There are two right-hand columns: *estimated cost* and *final cost*. On the top of the sheet are the address of the home, date of construction start, and other identification information. Among the many categories are: total cost of land and recording deeds; property taxes during ownership and construction; land surveying and building stakeout; builder's risk insurance for the specific property; cost of design or design alterations and plan printing; sewer hookup or septic system construction; water hookup construction or well and pump; hookup fees; gas service line costs; electric bills prior to sale; gas heating bills; winter construction costs such as snow plowing, covering hay, special heating, and concrete supplier's winter heating charges; and financing costs, include both the cost of the builder's own funds as well as borrowed funds.

Construction Cost Analysis
Cost Breakdown

OWNER **JOHN DOE**   BUILDER **JOHN DOE BUILDER**

MORTGAGOR

DATES **9/20/88, 10/5/88, 2/8/89**   ARCHITECT

JOB ADDRESS **482 HAPPY DRIVE**   PLAN NO. **VERNON 3**   ESTIMATOR

LEGAL **LOT 5, BLK. 3, VALLEY VIEW SUBD.**   SALESPERSON

ACCT. NO.		ACCOUNT TITLE OR OPERATION	SUBCONTRACTOR OR SUPPLIER	ESTIMATED COST		ACTUAL COST	
WP	1	PLANS & SPECIFICATIONS OR REVISION		500	—	400	—
WP	2	LAND COST: AT CLOSING		29,514	—	29,514	—
WP	3	ENGINEERING FEES		—		—	
WP	4	BUILDING PERMITS, INCL. HOUSE # & DECK PERMIT		389	—	389	—
WP	5	SEWER OR WATER FEES TO COMMUNITY		775	—	775	—
WP	6	SEWER – WATER LATERAL CONNECTIONS ± 50'		900	—	613	—
WP	7	SURVEY, STAKEOUT		235	—	235	—
WP	8	CONST. METER SERVICE – ELECTRIC	(20 + 14 + 11 + 10 = 55)	60	—	55	—
WP	9	BUILDER'S RISK INSURANCE, AFTER CANCELLATION		210	—	184	—
WP	10	TEMPORARY HEAT		200	—	172	—
WP	11	EXCAVATION		400	—	375	—
WP	12	BACKFILLING & ROUGH DRIVEWAY STONE		325	—	350	—
WP	13	GARAGE FLOOR GRAVEL		270	—	270	—
WP	14	FOUNDATION: CONCRETE		4900	—	4874	—
WP	15	BASEMENT WINDOW WELLS		11	—	11	—
WP	16	STEEL BAR & BEAMS (INCL. IN WP 14)		—		—	
WP	17	FOUNDATION INSULATION	(129 + 46 = 175)	175	—	175	—
WP	18	SIDING MATERIALS		1660	—	1720	—
WP	19	SPECIAL EXTERIOR TRIM		—		99	—
WP	20	ROOF TRUSSES		1300	—	1300	—
WP	21	FRAMING LUMBER & EXTERIOR TRIM MATERIAL		6500	—	6535	—
WP	22	FRAMING LABOR & EXTERIOR TRIM LABOR		6100	—	6100	—
WP	23	ENTRY DOORS & JAMBS		440	—	440	—
WP	24	STORM DOORS & HARDWARE		120	—	104	—
WP	25	WIND CAULKING & SEALING		35	—	35	—
WP	26	WINDOWS & PATIO DOORS (INCL. GRILLES)		2870	—	2849	—
WP	27	ROOFING (24 2/3 SQ. @ 45 =	1050 + 6 VENTS @ 5)	1095	—	1150	—
WP	28	GARAGE DOORS		575	—	594	—
WP	29	SIDING LABOR		1100	—	1115	—
WP	30	PLUMBING	(INC. WHIRLPOOL TUB @ 1050)	6935	—	6935	—
WP	31	HEATING		3600	—	3621	—
WP	32	ATTIC FAN		42	—	42	—
WP	33	ELECTRICAL		2510	—	2537	—
WP	34	GAS SERVICE LINE		—		—	
WP	35	PHONE PREWIRE		50	—	50	—
WP	36	BRICK – STONE INC. LABOR ON FIREPLACE	(61 + 5 + 209 = 275)	225	—	275	—
WP	37	FIREPLACE PARTS & INSTALLATION	(678 + 75 = 753)	700	—	753	—
WP	38	FLAT CONCRETE CONTRACT		2289	—	2111	—
WP	39	MOLDED MARBLE LAVATORIES		40	—	47	—

Figure 6.7 Construction Cost Analysis Sheet

ACCT. NO.		ACCOUNT TITLE OR OPERATION	SUBCONTRACTOR OR SUPPLIER	ESTIMATED COST		ACTUAL COST	
WP	40	TEMPORARY TOILET		—		—	
WP	41	BASEMENT STAIR LUMBER		165	—	181	—
WP	42	FLOOR MATERIAL, UNDERLAYMENT	(14 SHTS @ 8 + FELT 10)	140	—	145	—
WP	43	FLOOR LABOR, UNDERLAYMENT	(14 @ 3 + 4 + MISC.)	105	—	105	—
WP	44	DRYWALL & LABOR		3950	—	4260	—
WP	45	DRYWALL, FINISH SPRAY PAINT		200	—	200	—
WP	46	EXTERIOR FINISH CAULKING		150	—	182	—
WP	47	INSULATION		1130	—	1100	—
WP	48	FINISH HARDWARE		375	—	382	—
WP	49	INTERIOR TRIM MATERIAL		2600	—	2828	—
WP	50	INTERIOR TRIM LABOR		1900	—	1920	—
WP	51	PAINTING, EXTERIOR		1200	—	1200	—
WP	52	STAIN/VARNISH INTERIOR TRIM, INCL. WALL TOUCH UP		1400	—	1450	—
WP	53	KITCHEN CABINETS & VANITIES		1535	—	1482	—
WP	54	MIRRORS		120	—	122	—
WP	55	COUNTERTOPS		725	—	681	—
WP	56	TILE AROUND WHIRLPOOL TUB		140	—	200	—
WP	57	ELECTRICAL FIXTURES — ALLOWANCE		500	—	500	—
WP	58	SHOWER DOOR		170	—	185	—
WP	59	WEATHERSTRIP — THRESHOLDS		-0	—	15	—
WP	60	(RANGE — OVEN) — HOOD — FAN		480	—	495	—
WP	61	(DISHWASHER) WASHER — DRYER		240	—	243	—
WP	62	FLOORS, CERAMIC		300	—	220	—
WP	63	FLOOR FINISH — CARPETING ALLOWANCE 182 YDS.		2300	—	2300	—
WP	64	FLOOR FINISH, VINYL SHEET 40 YDS.		580	—	605	—
WP	65	FINAL GRADING & FINAL DRIVEWAY STONE		550	—	432	—
WP	66	DECK MATERIALS		400	—	395	—
WP	67	DECK LABOR		350	—	475	—
WP	68	GENERAL CLEAN UP & WINDOW CLEANING		250	—	175	—
WP	69	TRASH HAULING		100	—	125	—
WP	70	LOAN COSTS, INCL. BUILDER'S FUNDS — INTEREST		3250	—	2710	—
WP	71	LOAN COSTS, FEES & CLOSING COSTS		—		—	
WP	72	LANDSCAPING		—		—	
WP	73	TAXES, REAL ESTATE DURING OWNERSHIP PERIOD		500	—	555	—
WP	74	EXTERIOR PAVEMENTS		—		—	
WP	75	WELL		—		—	
WP	76	PUMP		—		—	
		SEPTIC SYSTEM		—		—	
NO MARKUP		STATE TRANSFER TAX ON REAL ESTATE	A-1	400	—	393	—
NO MARKUP		TITLE INSURANCE AT SALE CLOSING	A-1	280	—	254	—
		TOTAL COSTS TO BE MARKED UP (WP1-76)	A-2	102,855	—	102,672	—
		PROPOSED GROSS PROFIT MARKUP (@ 25%)	A-3	25,714	—	—	
		PROPOSED SALE PRICE (A-1) + (A-2) + (A-3)		129,249	—		
		(NOTE: NEAR SALE TIME, PRICE WAS INCREASED TO ALLOW FOR A RISING MARKET.)					
B-1		ACTUAL SALE W/O TRANSFER TAX & TITLE INSURANCE				130,353	—
B-2		NON SALES OVERHEAD — ACTUAL	(7.65% of B-1)			9972	—
B-3		SALES EXPENSE, ACTUAL	(3.15% of B-1) ┐21.22%			4100	—
B-4		PROFIT, NET, ACTUAL	(10.42% of B-1) ┘			13,609	—
B-5		ACTUAL SALE, INCL. TRANSFER TAX & TITLE INSURANCE				131,000	—

Figure 6.7 Construction Cost Analysis Sheet (cont'd)

The construction costs should be in categories that represent how you subdivide the costs of suppliers and subcontracts. For example, if you use one sub for the footing and another for the foundation wall, you will need two categories. Likewise, separate the cost of foundation excavation from the cost of foundation backfilling and rough driveway, even though you use the same sub for both operations. If you subdivide your rough lumber as I do, you will need a category for rough lumber and another for trusses. Keep costs of the siding labor subcontract separate from the rough framing carpentry and separate all siding materials from rough lumber costs. It is not necessary to separate mechanical costs (plumbing, heating, electrical) into rough and finish. Light fixture materials are separate. Don't forget sales taxes on materials. Separate painting costs into interior stain/varnish work, exterior work and drywall painting.

General clean-up and trash hauling are two more categories. Others that should be included are building permits; the state real estate sales tax paid by seller instead of buyer; title insurance costs; and any other costs you may incur at sale closing whether or not you have a broker or attorney.

For any labor items that are usually performed by you or a family member, be sure to enter these services at true market value. For clean-up work such as house cleaning; tub, shower, and window cleaning; and yard clean-up, I generally use $200 or $300 as the value of my company's labor. Trash hauling is hired out on a per-cubic-yard basis.

A construction site temporary toilet and dumpster rental might be required. Erosion-preventing plastic silt fencing might also be required. These should all be included in the cost breakdown sheet.

Leave space at the bottom of the sheet for total costs, markup percentage to yield overhead and net profit, final price, and asking price. Finally, you could break down your overhead into actual sales cost, supervision/expediting time, etc.

Low-Cost Ideas for Each Category of Construction

The following is a list of bidding and purchasing principles I have used successfully, beginning at the start of construction.

Surveying

Use a surveyor who is familiar with builders' work and the local area. Where the practice allows it and it is easy to do, I set my own excavation stakes to save money.

Excavation

The lowest-cost operators usually have the newest and largest machines. Working at a dollar rate per cubic yard or lineal foot is best, and an hourly rate is the second best deal. Lump sum bids are too high and reflect contingencies that are usually not encountered.

Foundation

In many regions, purchase of materials by the builder is common. Separate the work as much as practical:

• A separate contractor for the footing could save money.

- A structural steel supplier who sets the beams and columns upon delivery relieves the foundation wall sub of heavy work at lower cost.
- Consider hiring your own asphalt sprayer for dampproofing.
- A small sub could install outside foundation insulation or you could do it yourself in a couple of hours.

Flat Concrete

Some subs give a square-foot price for garage floor, for basement floor, porch, and per lineal foot of steps. Carefully calculate the exact areas and multiply to arrive at a total flatwork estimate. Usually extra gravel fill is an additional charge. As always, it is important to have an accurate material list.

In some regions, one sub will prepare the grade and forms for concrete, and another will place and finish the concrete furnished by the builder.

Rough Carpentry

Framers are usually fast-moving workers. Often they are undercapitalized; prompt payment, within one day after completion, can lower their bid. Alternately, they might offer a 5 percent quick-pay discount. At bid time, explain conditions that save them time and money such as prompt delivery of good materials, an electric power source, a detailed and complete lumber list, and a list of window rough openings and header sizes.

Most carpenter subs have not done any extensive labor-hour cost studies of their various tasks. They base bids on their own basic records or use memory and instinct. They often bid out framing on a per-square-foot basis, a fact that can sometimes be to your advantage.

You can use an estimating reference book, such as *Means Estimating Handbook* or *Means Productivity Standards*. Using my own observations while visiting job sites almost hourly, I developed my own set of labor-hours per task records. These are quoted as labor-hours per 1,000 square feet of floor for joists and plywood; per 100 lineal feet of exterior wall with sheathing; per 100 feet of interior partitions; per roof truss member; per 1,000 square feet of roof plywood; per 100 feet of roof overhang work; per window and door; per stairway; etc.

There is a great variation in productivity among different contractor subs and among regions of the country or within one state, and even sometimes (but rarely) within one county. R.S. Means Company publishes a number of cost data books for the various categories of construction, including *Means Building Construction Cost Data,* which provides cost data and information on trends in construction costs for all 50 states and Canada. These publications are updated annually.

Labor-hours can be 100 percent higher in the worst situation, as compared to the most productive sub. Find the range of productivity that fits your area. List the labor-hours needed to complete all framing tasks on your design in two columns—one for high productivity and one for low. Add these columns up for a range of total labor-hours needed on the entire framing job. Then multiply these hours times what the framing sub needs per labor-hour for wages, fringe benefits, taxes, insurance, and general overhead and profit to arrive at a range for the bids. Generally, the framing sub needs to realize a return of 50–100 percent over direct wages paid, plus compensation for any high-cost special equipment such as a fork lift truck or crane. The most basic analysis of labor hours that every builder should engage in is to record the total hours used to frame up each home built.

Case Study:
Variations in Framing Labor-Hours

The total hours on our 2,100-square-foot, two-story model varied from 160 to 200 hours using the same framing sub each time. Weather conditions and the composition of the framer's crew accounted for most of this variance. Nailing guns and a large fork lift were used by this sub, who also had some very efficient carpenters. They also used "tilt-up" framing techniques. The cost of the framing contract for labor and nails was about $6,000 four years ago.

Lumber

The cost of lumber is highly volatile. Often there is a seasonal peak, but don't anticipate price predictability. The carload cash price of studs and plywood per square or board foot is listed every Monday on the commodity page of the *Wall Street Journal*. Tracking this price can be of some help; at least you will know when lumber is cheap. The lumber dealers try to time their wholesale purchases somewhat to take advantage of weekly price variations.

A 10 percent rise in the cost of softwood framing lumber equals about a 1 percent rise in the cost of a new house. Concentrate on suppliers with a good number of builder customers. After you have a bid that matches your lumber list exactly, you may be able to shave just a little off of it. Try to reduce the bid from $6,587 to $6,500, for example. If $150,000 is your market niche maximum, your price of $145,000–$148,000 will give you some room to absorb $1000 or add $1000 in lumber cost fluctuation without losing prospects. These prices will vary depending on where you are working.

Roofing

Roofing subs are notoriously undercapitalized. Your willingness to pay for the materials directly will save money on the total roofing cost. Delivery of materials should include placing bundles of roofing at the roof top. Efficient roofers use an air power nailer that drives in a conventional round head nail.

A 250-pound asphalt or fiberglass shingle, instead of a 240-pound one, can prevent some wind damage, offer a longer warranty, and give you something to advertise in your sales brochure. The cost of this upgrade may be under $100.

Insulation

Get several bids based on bidder's visits to the rough home. This will allow for a greater chance of bidder accuracy than estimating from the plan, and many insulators prefer to visit the actual building first.

Siding

Shop around thoroughly for various types of siding and prices. If it is a factory product, buy it as close to the source as possible. With wood siding, you will need to find a carpenter to install siding by the lump sum or square (100 square feet of material). Furnish the nails to control quality, if possible. Siding specialists can cost less than using a framing sub.

Windows

Get bids for windows from direct factory distributors. Compare quality as well as price and check the differences in air/wind infiltration tests. Pre-stained wood sashes could be a savings overall if you know the actual cost of staining a sash on site. You may find it advantageous to purchase the sliding glass patio door elsewhere and to purchase the main and secondary entry doors or octagon windows from a third and fourth source. Here, too, you must consider the point of diminishing returns against the extra purchasing work.

Drywall

Many drywall subs are undercapitalized. You might get a slightly lower price by offering to pay for materials delivered and then to pay the contract balance promptly upon completion. Your material list will be an aid in checking bids or you may assist a bidder with it. I have paid $200–$300 extra for having the drywall sub spray the walls with a quality, washable off-white paint. There is no other way to paint the drywall so cheaply. Have it included in the drywall work, if at all possible.

Interior Trim Materials

Pre-hung doors are the most efficient way to go, but casing miters should be cut on the job. Find a good builder-oriented supplier for doors, casings, base, closet parts, and moldings. It may be cheaper to purchase oak boards and underlayment elsewhere.

Interior Carpentry

Often interior carpentry subs will bid work on a square-foot basis – $1.50 per square foot, for example. This approach usually doesn't reflect the true labor involved in the work. It is often too high, because of the value engineering applied to your design.

In the same way that a labor-hour-per-task record was compiled for rough carpentry, you can calculate a range of total hours that are involved in interior work. Read the material that applies to this in reference book time records – then do your own detective work to find the number of hours or tenths of an hour needed to set a pre-hung door, case one side, case a window, install 100 feet of base, install each cabinet box, etc.

You could furnish a list of work for bidding purposes such as: set 12 pre-hung doors and apply casing, case 13 windows, install 350 feet of base, etc. If you have a finished example of your design (your own home, for example), a visit to it will make this sub realize the true extent of the work and the level of quality required.

If there is a decent amount of floor underlayment to be installed, consider a specialist for this work only. He or she will usually give you a square-foot price over the phone.

This use of pre-hung doors and minimal trim can reduce finish carpentry to a semi-skilled job of 30 to 40 labor-hours. I have saved a good deal of money on several homes by having a part-time, hourly-paid carpenter come in evenings and weekends to install doors, casings and other highly skilled work. I have performed the simpler work myself; I could have hired part-time apprentices for closet shelving, basement stairs, and porch trim. I have also laid the 1/4″ plywood underlayment and for a few dollars per sheet, our vinyl installer completes the underlayment stapling to satisfy his requirements. Make sure every sub is covered by insurance, either by you or by him- or herself.

I have also installed hardware, mirrors, and shower doors. However, I would not recommend getting this involved with the finish carpentry or with any other trade. It takes you away from the more important tasks of overall job management, market research, and site selection. Be sure to include the value of your on-site labor in the cost breakdown sheet.

Countertops

Use a specialty sub — one who often has his or her own shop. This is usually not a job for the carpenter.

Floor Covering and Tile

The carpeting allowance included in the sale price of the home can be based on the low cost of carpeting purchased directly from the mill, including shipping, pad, sales tax, and installation by your own carpet layer sub. Find a good and reasonable installer who works by the yard and will measure the home and pick up and pre-cut the order from the truck terminal.

A store manager at a chain tile store will usually calculate the vinyl yardage required from the plans. Monitor this calculation to avoid excess waste. I would pick up the tile materials and store it at the home, ready for installation by a sub who works by the square yard of material used. This type of sub does a lot of installations for various floor covering dealers. Be sure to hire an installer who does neat, well-fitting, quality work.

I usually hire a small ceramic tile contractor who operates out of his home with his son and a few employees. He was recommended by a tile supply house. He bids work by the square foot and by the lump sum for a basic tile selection. We stay with traditional, tile-like colors and patterns in the lower price range.

Painting

As stated earlier, I have interior drywall surfaces textured and spray painted in one operation by a drywall sub. He leaves a quart of material for touch up after completion. I highly recommend this approach. If you can't find a drywaller to include this service, hire a sub to spray the walls right after the drywaller leaves. This is a critical path job — interior carpentry can't begin until the paint is dry.

Interior wood stain and varnish work can be handled by a lump-sum sub, by you, or by part-time, hourly people. Use the lump sum sub's bid for your cost breakdown sheet. The most efficient procedure is to wipe or spray on stain, seal and then sand all materials before installation. Pre-hung doors can be handled more easily after setting, but in some locales, even these can be stained before installation. Nail putty and varnish work is completed after carpentry.

I always use prefinished cabinets. The factory finish is always superior and sometimes the construction is, too. Be sure to observe a painter's work, both completed and in progress, before hiring him or her for stain/varnish work.

I employ several strategies to lower exterior painting costs. The rain gutters and storm doors are factory enameled. Roof overhang fascia and soffit materials are pre-primed before installation, either by me or by the lumber yard. I use siding that is factory primed or stained by the lumber yard whenever possible. Caulking is done by the painter, by me, or by part-time help. One advantage of aluminum or vinyl siding is that caulking, nails, labor and siding (not requiring painting) are included in one price. I found caulking specialists to be too expensive. An exterior painting sub can caulk for less.

There are a lot of figures to pull together for the total painting cost estimate. Several separate categories will help. It's easy to forget something here.

Cabinets

I generally use prefinished, factory-built cabinets from a large nationwide manufacturer. I get the best price by dealing with a large builder-oriented distributor. Discounts off list prices can run as high as 60 percent.

Finish Hardware

The main cost in finish hardware is locksets. Find a source offering low prices for volume builder business on locksets and then include rail/brackets, door stops and other items in the package. I usually buy bath hardware from a large home center store. Use materials that are popular, low-cost and easy to install.

Mirrors and Shower Doors

You can use one or two suppliers for mirrors and shower doors, and either the suppliers or the trim carpenter can install them — whatever works best. I use 1/4″ square edge plate mirrors.

Appliances

Consumer Reports magazine can make you aware of the best buys and problems in appliances. I usually include just a dishwasher (not an expensive one with complicated controls) and an oven/range (either self cleaning or continuous cleaning). The electric sub usually includes the range hood in his work. Choose safe, popular colors in a lower, but not the lowest, price range. Suppliers that offer the lowest builder prices are usually statewide distributors for appliance stores or the "builder division" of a large nationwide chain of retail stores. A good service setup is important for warranty work. Include sales tax and delivery cost in this category, even though you may save dollars by delivery with your van or truck.

Mechanicals

Mechanical subs are better capitalized and organized than some of the others we've discussed. Equipment and fixtures can fail or leak, so you need a sub with a reputation for prompt service on repairs during the warranty period. When comparing the costs of higher-efficiency furnaces that have power exhaust venting with those that have only gravity exhaust, don't forget the cost of the gravity vent. I prefer the power vented models, but avoid the extra cost of the highest-priced models that add just a few points to the fuel efficiency.

If you choose a very low-water-use toilet, make sure it will do the job with one flush, not two. It is common for low-flush models to require more than one flush, which contradicts the purpose for buying such a model in the first place. One luxury lavatory faucet is affordable, if it is used only in the first floor powder room.

Light Fixtures

I generally use $500 as a total allowance for light fixtures, including sales tax. Determine whether the electric sub will include a door chime or range hood in his bid. The most obvious and important fixtures are at the front entry, foyer, formal dining and dinette. You may have to purchase these fixtures from a large supply specialist. You can buy other fixtures, such as hall lights and side door entries, less expensively at do-it-yourself home centers. Bath lights over the vanity are another special spot. Efficient and attractive lighting is important here. I have often purchased fixtures for one house from three different sources.

A final note about saving costs in construction: You can sometimes receive an additional discount—perhaps 2 to 5 percent—from suppliers who offer a model-home discount. Some suppliers offer these discounts based on the assumption that model homes will be seen by a greater segment of the general public. Suppliers who might offer such a discount include siding, window, cabinets, appliance, or furnace dealers.

Orders and Subcontracts

Very large builders may use formal contracts for subs that run up to eight pages long. Small builders often contract with just a handshake, or a bid list and a handshake. Be sure you have at least a bid sheet so the precise nature of the job is well understood by both parties. When dealing with a new sub, check references for clients, suppliers, and insurers as soon as possible.

Be sure to itemize and acknowledge all phone bids in writing. This is easier to accomplish with suppliers than with subs, because many subs avoid paperwork like the plague. Mechanical subs usually furnish a detailed proposal, but everything must be checked thoroughly. Errors and omissions are not uncommon with subs in any category.

Some subs, such as carpenters and drywall contractors, tend to operate with verbal or handwritten, incomplete bids. They don't want to be bothered with formal contracts. Even if you know the sub well, a change in his or her personal life or fortune can put you at risk. Let your judgment be your guide, but use a comprehensive writing covering important points whenever possible. You could have the sub initial your copy of your combination bid/specification sheet that you furnish at bid time. For example, to the framing carpenter you could include a nailing schedule, call out who furnishes nails, who furnishes glue, what exterior trim is to be (or not to be) installed, some schedule for completion or minimum number of labor hours to be applied to the job weekly, time of payment, approval by inspector, etc.

Don't come on too strong with a formal contract. An incompetent or dishonest worker will be scared away, but a conscientious, skilled sub can also be scared away or insulted by what he may interpret as distrust. Go over examples of subcontracts from builder associations, legal form suppliers, and textbooks for ideas. Many of these are written for large, commercial projects where they are quite common, but their use in home building is not so common. Nonetheless, these documents are a good source of ideas. Generally, builders who use written contracts save 3–5 percent in costs.

Case Study:
Lack of Written Subcontracts Won't Protect You from Unethical Subs

I once hired a new foundation sub to work on a duplex townhouse. I received and accepted a phone bid for footings, concrete block basement, garage foundation walls and steel beams. He began work but claimed to have forgotten his written proposal that I had requested he bring with him on the first day. He also forgot the proposal on the second day. After he did not bring a proposal on the third day, we had a stern discussion. He had been trying to raise his price, claiming that he had added a few extras to the work already finished. He had not presented me any proposals for extra work prior to that time. Then he asked to see the bids of his competitors and said that he would work for the price of the second lowest bid. I held firm, the job was completed, and I paid all his material suppliers (there were four or five) to protect myself from possible supplier lien rights. The balance remaining from his bid was paid to him. The total cost was reasonable. A lesson was learned here about allowing a new sub to start work without a written proposal. I should have had a proposal of my own ready for him to sign on the first day he claimed to have forgotten to bring his own proposal.

Summary

"Let us never negotiate out of fear, but let us never fear to negotiate."
—John F. Kennedy

The material in this chapter should help you in your negotiations with subcontractors and suppliers, and also help you to organize your business with respect to obtaining bids, performing quantity takeoffs, itemizing costs, and saving money. Chapter 7 provides more discussion on cost issues—specifically financing—and insurance.

Key Points
• Sources for finding subcontractors include suppliers; lumber yards; local builders' associations; the yellow pages; and neighborhoods where new homes are being built.
• To bring a spec home to the market at the lowest possible cost, layers of profit must be eliminated.
• A complete list of materials allows for more control of the project and makes it easy to shop for materials.
• Options for creating a lumber list include using a lumber listing service; creating your own list; or first using a service and from that, learning to create your own list.

- The process of creating a lumber list provides a good opportunity to apply the principles of value engineering to analyze lumber costs.
- Most subs and suppliers will reward repeat business with better service and personal attention to problems.
- A comprehensive cost breakdown sheet can provide both estimates and final costs for categories of construction to give you greater insight into and control of your business. A rough version can also serve as your initial feasibility study.
- Even if you do not use a contract, be sure to have at least a bid sheet so the precise nature of the job is understood by both parties.
- With a written contract, get all changes initialed by the parties, and include references to any missing items covered elsewhere such as workmanship standards, starting time, continuity of work, insurance certificates, and hold-harmless clauses.

Chapter 7
Project Financing & Insurance

An understanding of project financing and insurance is crucial for any spec builder, no matter how small his or her business is. Unless you have vast amounts of cash on hand (and even if you do), you will undoubtedly need to finance at least one project—and all projects will require some kind of insurance. Your first consideration before embarking on a spec home project should be: Where will the money come from?

Case Study:
Discovering the True Percentage Cost of a Construction Loan

Many years ago I financed 75 percent of the final value of my first spec home with a bank construction loan at 7 percent interest, plus 1 percent for the closing/processing or initiation fee, plus a small charge for an extra mortgage title insurance policy. The bank allowed construction to go forward without a prepaid survey after foundation work, which is normally required by all construction loans. After the sale agreement was reached, we furnished a copy of the buyer's survey for his lender for our bank's files. By most standards in the 1960s, this was a good financing deal overall. After the sale was completed, I went over all bank financing costs and realized that interest paid out at 7 percent on funds withdrawn was exactly equal to the other fixed loan costs. So, in effect, I had paid 14 percent interest on the funds borrowed. I vowed to build up my finances so I could finance all construction and thereby keep the 14 percent for myself.

Case Study:
Loan Committees' Misunderstandings Can Cause Approval Delays

Several years later I applied for a construction loan from a savings and loan that had served me for my previous spec home. Spring was approaching fast. I was anxious to get started but approval of my loan was not forthcoming. After repeated phone calls I discovered the problem. The loan committee did not like part of the floor plan. They felt that having the formal dining area near the head of the entry foyer stair would impede traffic to the main living areas of the home, making the home difficult to sell. I submitted a 1/2-inch scale drawing of that portion of the home with a large dining set in place. It demonstrated that even a large dining set would allow for four feet of walking space. I received loan approval, but precious weeks had slipped away. This was the last home I financed with a construction loan.

Financing Cost as a Percentage of the Sale Price

"A banker is a guy who lends you his umbrella when it isn't raining."
—Anonymous

The smaller builder is usually at a disadvantage when borrowing money compared to a larger competitor. The smaller builder pays more for financing costs because he lacks clout.

In times of "normal" interest rates, total financing can cost 2-1/2 percent to 3 percent of the home's sale price. The high rates of the 1980s raised this percentage cost considerably. At the interest rates of early 1994, using the lowest-cost financing techniques, it was possible for a small builder to lower financing costs to 1-1/2 percent of the home's sale price. This low percentage will put you ahead of most of your competitors, both large and small.

Various Financing Systems

The least costly financing system, and the one that offers you the most control, involves borrowing on your other assets. It could be an open-ended mortgage on an otherwise debt-free personal residence. A loan from a securities broker or bank is a better idea, using your portfolio of stocks, bonds, or mutual funds as collateral.

Using your own hoard of cash (assuming you have one) may seem to be the best and least expensive way to finance spec homes; but then you have no financing costs to deduct from your business income. This may make no overall difference on your total income tax bill, but by using your own cash, you convert what could have been interest or dividend income into business income, thereby increasing the amount of self employment tax. For example, if this amounts to $3,000 in additional business income per home and $3,000 less investment income, your self-employment tax will increase by about $400—until you reach the maximum level, where this extra business income applies to a Medicare tax of about $50.

All of the above involves starting out with a bit of money. If you are operating with insufficient cash or net worth, then make this financial level your first goal. Until that time, here are some other alternatives.

Developing a Bank Line of Credit

If you obtain a line of credit at a bank, you may be asked to pledge your home and the one you are building, along with other assets. Try to avoid the cumbersome details, approvals, waiting, and draws of a construction loan.

Borrowing on the Lot

At times a subdivider will take back a mortgage that he or she is willing to subordinate to the construction loan, which follows later. The subdivider can create this second mortgage position by filing this mortgage after the bank files theirs. You could be financing 100 percent of the costs this way. Usually the subdivider will be willing to settle for fewer dollars if you cash him or her out before construction begins. You could consider combining the subdivider's loan with funds from non-construction loan sources.

Engaging in a Joint Venture

You might consider a joint venture with a wealthy speculator who provides occasional management advice and supplies all the funds for land and building. Even in the best situation, however, the builder loses a great deal of control here. I have heard horror stories—cases in which the moneyed partner took 60 percent of the profit just for supplying the money. The builder in essence becomes a "share cropper."

The Construction Loan

Although most builders, when starting out, will need a construction loan, it should be your last resort. Be careful to research the lending institution you're considering, and get a line on the reputation of several loan officers from real estate brokers. There are many ways to be led down a blind alley. You need a loan officer with a reputation for being able to evaluate your situation quickly and accurately so that time is not lost awaiting approval from an institution that will probably turn down your application. You could apply to several institutions at the same time, but this can backfire on you in the long run.

When applying for a loan, remember that first impressions are important. Look sharp and be sharp. Along with the plans and specifications, you will be asked to submit a cost breakdown list of subs and suppliers, including their names. Remember, however, that this is confidential information, important to your success—so be cautious. If you live in a state that requires the lender to disburse all funds directly to subs and suppliers, you should ensure that your breakdown sheet is accurate. However, you might want to somewhat overstate the cost of work categories that you execute yourself. For example, if you install the footings or foundations, a relatively high cost for this item releases extra funds early in the building process for you to use as capital and provides a hedge against items you have underestimated.

In states where the builder is required by the lender to disburse the funds and be reimbursed at four intervals during construction, it is easier to make upward adjustments to the actual expected cost categories. This way, you can reduce the amount allocated for gross profit—showing as little as 10 percent for overhead and profit instead of the actual 20 percent or more.

Keep in mind that the lender's breakdown sheet exposes the structure and efficiency of your operation to the eyes of the world. While the lender knows the information is confidential, I have heard of cases where brokers and even buyers gain access to some of this information. Slightly raising the expected costs of early construction categories such as foundation, lumber, and framing will provide you with extra working capital in the early stages of construction. However, lenders are on guard against any builder "getting ahead" by receiving more funds than have actually gone into construction at any point. The lender always needs enough funds on hand to complete the home should the builder die, go bankrupt, or leave the country prior to completion of the home. But some adjustments in the cost breakdown sheet furnished to the lender can be made, from both ethical and practical standpoints. If you choose to make changes that raise costs and lower gross profit, remember that each draw on funds will contain fewer dollars in the gross profit category if you show a 10 percent gross profit instead of 20 percent.

Be prepared to furnish the lender with your personal and business financial statements along with copies of the past two or three years' income tax returns. Get complete data on all loan costs: application fee, initiation/closing fee, interest rate, appraiser and credit report costs, title insurance, extra survey work, special assessment letters, and so on. Many of these items and costs are not required when using the other various non-construction loan financing systems.

Finally, with regard to any loan, request that the lending institution furnish you with copies of all documents that you will be signing at a time prior to the closing time or date. You will then have time to study these documents to carefully determine what you are getting into — away from the fast-moving, slightly chaotic atmosphere of many loan closings.

Don't expect to obtain a non-recourse loan, where your default allows the lender to repossess only the real estate pledged and not your other assets. This type of loan is usually available only for large commercial real estate ventures.

Using Your Own Funds

Despite the extra self-employment tax consequences of using your own funds, this financing system is the easiest to implement. It is used often by a few large, older, well-established home building firms.

Be careful to quantify the true "opportunity cost" of using your own funds. You could calculate this financing cost based on the return available from long-term, BBB-rated corporate bonds. You could use the rate of return available from the place where these funds would normally be employed or the historical rate of return from an investment in a stock market index. In any event, don't assume that you could earn only a low money market rate of return from these funds. After all, liquidity will be non-existent for several months and the risk is greater than in the money market. Some real estate development guide books have set the interest rate value of the developer's own funds as high as 15 percent. One telephone company had their engineers use 18 percent as cost of funds when they calculated costs in the late 1970s.

Don't forget to calculate the cost of your own funds when borrowing for a construction loan. The construction loan amount will never cover all costs; it is easy to forget that you may have tied up $30,000 in the land three months prior to start of construction.

Insurance   Although you are undoubtedly aware that as a spec builder you will need to obtain insurance, this section provides some guidelines and principles to consider when researching and shopping for insurance.

Insurance for the House

The best builder's risk insurance is one that covers all risks: basement collapse, theft, vandalism, umbrella coverage for any uninsured subs, and so on. Carefully determine what protection you will definitely need and shop for a package that best suits your needs. Consider a deductible of $1,000, which should lower the premium. In some locations, theft insurance may cost a high premium. You will have to weigh this high premium against a "worst case" loss through theft.

Be sure to consult with agencies that cater to home building firms. Because rates and practices for insurance vary widely from company to company, shop around for the best deal. The most comprehensive policies are offered on properties that the builder will either live in or keep for investment. Keeping your business liability insurance with the same firm that holds your builder's risk policy on each home can help. The premium covers a one-year period and returns a short rate, cancellation-prorated premium when the property is sold prior to the one-year period. Often the insurance company will pay a bonus refund if your buyer continues to insure the home with the same company.

The insurance industry is more concerned with large construction projects than with the construction of single-family homes, because the larger premiums are earned from larger projects. Some insurance officials do not fully understand the application of insurance to small builders, especially in the area of liability. Double coverage of the same risk, with two different premiums or in two policies, is something to be wary of. One insurance company can, in effect, earn two premiums for the same coverage.

Finally, if your annual home building volume is large enough, consider how a "reporting form" master policy can save annual costs. In this system, you will have an ongoing policy with premiums that are determined by your monthly reports of construction in progress.

Your policy should begin as soon as your risk exposure to the home actually starts—that is soon enough. Your risk exposure begins when you have created a structure that can either be damaged by fire or forces of nature or cause injury to the public. But even an open basement excavation, without any construction, can expose you to liability if a child is injured while playing there.

Insurance for the Builder: Public Liability and Workers' Compensation

The area of builder's liability is more complex than builder's risk. It is also the area that represents the greatest risk to the builder's fortune. The following are two examples that illustrate the importance of builder's insurance. Working without proper liability coverage and completed operations coverage can be extremely dangerous. Liability insurance covers injury to another person or another person's property. Completed operations coverage is essentially liability coverage for completed work that extends beyond completion and payment to the builder.

America's legal system has created a situation where such insurance coverage can be very expensive. The cost of liability coverage is now so high that you would need to spread this cost over more than one or two homes built each year for it to be affordable and for you to have competitive costs. Because of the rising costs of insurance, many builders operate with incomplete or no liability coverage.

In addition to completed operations and general liability insurance, you will need some umbrella coverage for subs you hire at the last moment without the assurance of an insurance certificate. For some reason, this umbrella coverage is easier to obtain if you are going to continue owning the home after completion. Then it becomes part of the homeowner's policy.

The cases described below illustrate the extreme danger of being without liability coverage and completed operations coverage.

Case Study:
Accidents Can Have Broad Insurance Consequences

A plumbing contractor's employee took a bad fall into the basement of an unfinished home while descending down a crude ladder. The ladder had been built by the carpenter who worked on the home. As a result of the accident, the plumbing worker suffered permanent disability. By the time the legal dust had settled, the insurance companies of the carpenter, the plumbing contractor, and the builder had all paid out a good deal of money. The homeowner was left with the still-remaining balance of the court-awarded damages.

Case Study:
Claims Settled in Court Can Lead to Surprisingly
Large Settlements

The owner of a brick home that was being built pressured the builder into using a brick from a manufacturer with whom the builder was not familiar. After months of occupancy, the brick surface started to erode when rain or other water hit the brick. The owner insisted that the builder remove and replace the bricks with a more durable product. The cost was about $12,000. The owner also insisted that the extensive foundation plantings also be replaced. This was an additional cost of $9,000. At this, the builder balked. The case went to a court trial, and the court decided in favor of the owner at treble damages — $65,000 cost to the builder. It was unpleasant, but far less costly than a permanent injury to a worker or visiting neighbor. This case also illustrates the wisdom of keeping problems out of court.

Insurance for Subcontractors

Inform your subs early on that you require a current insurance certificate covering workers' compensation and $300,000 to $500,000 of public liability. Some subs comply readily with this request; others are more lax, or on occasion may even lie about coverage that they no longer have because of the high cost. Your insurer can audit your books and require that you pay the premiums for any uninsured subs. If you can get the name of the sub's insurance company, a phone call might reveal where you stand. The system of furnishing proof of insurance has room for improvement.

Sometimes insurance companies cannot decide whether to base the premium on contract prices that include materials or on prices that do not include materials. This is another reason to pay separately for the sub's materials. Strangely, many premiums are based on autos or trucks that are insured elsewhere rather than on the sub's payroll or value of the work done.

All in all, liability insurance is an enigmatic area. It seems most of us are in the dark and never quite sure if we are paying twice for the same coverage. Workers' compensation insurance is easy to follow, but premium rates vary tremendously from state to state. You may need the assistance of an experienced attorney and/or insurance consultant. Disastrous accidents rarely happen, but just one could change your life forever.

One idea you can always use to lower premium costs is to raise the deductible as high as you are comfortable with. You could live with a disaster that puts a strain on you for three to six months, but longer-term strains must be protected against.

Hedging Against Rising Mortgage Rates

Rapidly rising mortgage rates can have a negative effect on the value of a spec home under construction. The number of buyers who qualify for payments with higher monthly interest rates diminishes greatly, while market forces lower the price you can obtain for the home. Each one-point rise in mortgage rates can lower the sale value of a home by 4 to 6 percent.

There are ways to protect yourself, for a price, if you feel strongly that rates are going to run up. Such strategies include taking a short position in some corporate bonds, buying a put option on some interest rate futures, or taking a short position in treasury bond futures. As interest rates rise, these security derivatives increase greatly in value and the security gains balance against losses in the value of the home. If interest rates don't rise as expected, you lose the cost of your security option—the effect is something like an insurance premium. A good investment broker can explain all the details; but keep this strategy as a last resort. There are more losers than winners in the security derivatives markets.

Figure 7.1 shows notes from my own study of the effect of rising mortgage rates on new home sales prices from several years ago.

Case Study:
A Possible Strategy: Mortgage Buy-Downs

I have never used hedge positions but could have used their help in the early 1980s. I took on a land contract mortgage position at 11 percent interest to turn a sale on a home. The contract ran for a year, at which time mortgage rates were going toward 15 percent. The buyer could not qualify at those rates, so I renewed the contract for one more year at 12-1/2 percent. During that time, I could have obtained rates of over 15 percent for a money market investment instead of having my working capital tied up in an unmarketable security at this lower rate. At the end of the second year, I found a 12-1/2 percent permanent mortgage for the buyer and was finally paid out. If I had used a security hedge, profits from it could have been used to "buy down" a mortgage for my buyer.

Creative Buyer Financing

Creative financing describes an unusual financing technique wherein the seller pays something toward the buyer's loan, either in the form of payments to the lender or in a loan of money directly to the buyer. This approach is not needed most of the time, unless you have made some poor choices in your spec home offering. During times of wildly high mortgage rates, you may have to resort to some form of creative financing to sell a spec home, even when you have made all the right choices.

Sometimes a buyer cannot qualify for a large enough first mortgage, so the builder may offer to fill in the gap by taking a second mortgage. Don't use this strategy unless it is the only way to sell the home. Besides tying up your working capital, you end up with a weak security, marketable only to opportunists at a heavy discount. This discount is a risk to keep in mind when considering your gross profit margin. Make sure your second mortgage puts limits on the amount of the first mortgage or your position will be very weak.

Taking a first mortgage for a one-year period when the buyer has a large down payment may be a solution, but if the buyer can't refinance in one year, you are stuck with the nasty foreclosure process to free up your working capital.

Example I

Value of home: $130,000. Buyer qualifies for $100,000 mortgage.

At a rate of 10-1/4%, monthly principal and interest for 30-year fixed mortgage = $896.11.

At a rate of 10-3/4%, the same $896.11 payment for monthly principal and interest for 30-year fixed mortgage covers a mortgage of $96,000, or $4,000 less.

Market value might adjust from $130,000 to $126,000 or a drop of 3.08% for 1/2 point rise in mortgage interest rates or 6% drop per 1 point rise in rates. But this would be the maximum drop in value—it could likely be only a fraction of that.

Example II

Home at 3434 W. Happy Lane.

Value in 1982 with mortgage rates at 16% = $100,000.

Value in 1984 with mortgage rates at 12-1/2% = $120,000.

$20,000 \div 120,000 = 16\text{-}2/3\%$ drop $\div$ 3-1/2 point rise = 4.76% drop per point rise.

Conclusion

Each rise of one (1) point in mortgage interest rates will lower the sales value of a new home by 1-1/2% to 6%.

Figure 7.1 Study on the Effect of Rising Mortgage Rates on New Home Sale Prices

The best technique involves buying down the mortgage rate at closing with a lump sum payment from the seller to the lender. This payment is large enough to increase the yield to an overall market rate of return for the lender when the time duration of the mortgage is factored in. Lending institutions are very aware of the mathematics involved. You should fully understand the time value of money and the present value of a future stream of income to avoid overpaying for a buy-down. Also, you should be aware of the trends, as discussed in top-flight financial journals.

Often buy-downs are available only in large lots of $500,000 to $1,000,000 mortgages. You may have to sign up with a real estate brokerage firm that purchases buy-down commitments in large packages, or join with several other small builders to buy a package. You should be aware of the possible need for a buy-down before the start of construction and make some arrangements.

During times of very high interest rates, building costs drop because of a great lack of business. Savings in construction costs can be applied to partial payment of buy-down costs, and profit margins can be reduced to cover the balance of buy-down costs. In this way you can continue building, rather than shutting down or having to turn to another field such as remodeling.

Summary

It is evident that a certain degree of planning is necessary for financing and insuring a spec building project. This is not an area in which to take "short cuts": it is much too dangerous to work without proper insurance or dependable financing. Lowering the cost of financing can be a long-term goal.

The next chapter covers the various aspects of scheduling and supervision.

Key Points
- Small builders tend to pay more for financing than larger builders.
- In times of "normal" interest rates, total financing can cost 2-1/2% to 3% of the home's sale price.
- Financing options include using your own cash; borrowing on your other assets; using a bank line of credit; borrowing on the lot; engaging in a joint venture; and obtaining a construction loan. The construction loan should be your last resort.
- The best builder's risk insurance is one that covers all risks: basement collapse, theft, vandalism, umbrella coverage for any uninsured subs, etc.
- Your insurance policy should begin as soon as your risk exposure to the home starts.
- Liability insurance covers injury to another person or another person's property. Completed operations coverage is essentially liability insurance for completed work that extends beyond completion and payment to the builder. Working without both types of coverage is extremely dangerous.
- Require subs to carry (and prove) coverage for workers' compensation and $300,000 to $500,000 of public liability.
- During times of very high mortgage rates, you may have to use creative financing—the best technique involves buying down the mortgage rate at closing with a lump sum payment from seller to lender.

Chapter 8
Scheduling & Supervision

The process of scheduling and supervision can be the most challenging aspect of building. Obtaining the appropriate permits, maintaining good relationships with subcontractors, scheduling the various stages of a project, managing construction, and paying bills are all essential to the smooth running of a spec building business.

"Homes are like babies: fun to conceive, but hell to deliver." – Anonymous

Utility Services and Building Permits

Either before or during your application for a building permit, you should apply for utility services. Underground electric, telephone, and natural gas services cannot be applied for too soon. Water and sewer service availability should also be confirmed before applying for the building permit. In fact, that service availability should have been confirmed before you purchased the site.

Many building departments have a printed list of the documents required for permit application. This list might call for two or three sets of plans, two sets of a home location survey by a registered land surveyor, copies of an energy/heat loss calculation form, and a completed permit application form. Speedy issuance of the permit depends partly on your submission of complete documents. You can make a good first impression with the building inspector if you provide complete and professional plans and application documents. Inspectors may monitor your work more suspiciously if your work looks sloppy and incomplete before the permit is even issued.

If you follow the approval of your permit carefully, you may be able to complete foundation excavation work before you actually pick up and pay for the permit. Then you could possibly request a footing inspection on the day you pay for the permit.

Post your permit at the job site before the building inspector arrives for the first inspection. The better permit forms allow for good communication – they have boxes on the card in which the inspector can initial his approval or comment otherwise. Then there is never a need to call the building department to determine whether inspection has been actually made as scheduled or is approved.

Permit fees can vary widely from state to state and even county to county. Be sure to get some information about permit costs before you buy land in a new political jurisdiction.

Builder as Worker/Subcontractor

From a business point of view, you are wise to *not* perform any actual construction work. Your time and attention can then be focused on fine-tuning your overall business, improving design, doing market research, searching for your next building site, increasing your sources for better and lower-cost suppliers and subs, and carefully supervising construction.

Many times just the opposite is the case. Small builders often try to do everything and end up being inefficient subs whose work is not of the highest quality. Meanwhile, other aspects of their operation suffer — designs are poor or not cost-effective, purchasing is not thorough, and so on. Whatever they save on subcontractor costs is often lost in other areas of their spec home endeavor.

If a builder were to execute all subcontracted labor on a home, except for the mechanical trades, he or she could save 20 to 25 percent of all construction costs. This amounts to less than the gross profit margin of the total finished package, without considering that the builder will need at least one hourly assistant whose cost will reduce the savings sharply. More difficult to quantify is the cost of the increased time it takes for a one- or two-person crew of non-specialists to do everything.

If you have the skill for some carpentry, painting, or bricklaying, and are fairly efficient, you might attempt a few small jobs. These jobs should last no more than one or two days, so you will not be taken away from the business end of building for very long. Examples of these types of jobs are laying brick around the fireplace, installing floor underlayment, and installing basement stairs.

If you are building three to four or more spec homes per year, concentrate on the business. Sublet all construction work. The extra money you could earn by performing the work yourself is proportionately small after taxes. Construction work is not the best physical exercise. Get your exercise by walking, running, or swimming.

The Subcontractor Versus the Hourly Employee

Some builders employ their own carpentry or foundation crews on a full-time basis. After a number of years, they usually discover that it is more cost-effective to use outside subcontractors. Although you may have enough work to keep a crew busy year-round, these builder crews can be very inefficient and often develop into a bureaucratic "old soldier's home."

You might consider hiring an hourly "jack of all trades" who is paid periodically like a subcontractor. There are several dangers in this practice. First, the Internal Revenue Service is watching. You could be liable for tax withholding, Social Security payments, unemployment insurance, and penalties. Often these hourly subcontractors are really employees in the eyes of the IRS. A carpenter sub who builds an outdoor deck at $20 per hour under your supervision is really not a subcontractor, as the carpenter who agrees to build the deck for $500 is. Also, in each of these situations, insurance coverage for public liability and workers' compensation must be provided.

You may find yourself in the "hourly sub" situation when real subcontractors are difficult to find. Here are several ideas that could increase the availability of bona fide, insured subs:

- Consider helping a good tradesperson to set himself up as a sub with insurance, employee tax connections, and some capital, in return for preferential service to your jobs and some small share of business profit and control.
- Offer a fixed bonus to a sub for service within five days of notice.
- Simply enlarge the number of subs you have in your file.

Communicating with Subcontractors

"The biggest problem in the world could have been solved when it was small." — Walter Bynner

Be sure to discuss your workmanship standards with each new sub, since he or she may be accustomed to doing things in a way that pleases another builder. Take the time to define the parameters of a good working relationship. For example, determine the best time of day to phone each sub.

One good idea is to have a plywood "bulletin board" set inside the garage of the home. Here you can leave instructions for the subs and they can leave their questions for you. A space for anyone's suggestions could be of help.

Many subs are aggravated and inconvenienced when a builder comes to them with a verbal list of complaints. A written punch list accomplishes more with less friction. You might arrange a time to discuss the list at a later time if necessary.

Another thing to keep in mind is that loud radio music on the site can create all kinds of problems — it can even drive other subs away. It can also aggravate neighbors if you are building in an established neighborhood. Again, communicate such restrictions from the very beginning.

In your encounters with various subcontractors, you will meet people who are easy to work with and you will meet people who are difficult to work with. Patience, tact, diplomacy, firmness, and fairness are all essential in communicating with subs. Be an enthusiastic leader, but be aware that being too friendly with a sub can dull your objectivity and weaken your authority.

Avoiding Scheduling and Supervision Problems

The following discussion is actually a detailed list of suggestions for improving the scheduling, supervision, and quality of work at the various stages of construction. Some of the guidelines listed here have also been mentioned earlier in the book.

Keep in mind that certain materials, such as windows and roof trusses, must be ordered well ahead of the time of their actual delivery to the job site. These are materials that are not in stock — they are manufactured after being ordered. Keep in mind that 65% of all delays occur in the first 15 days of construction.

Excavation and Foundation

Consider the benefits of earlier-than-normal spring starts: lower prices, availability of subs, and having the product ready for sale during prime marketing season. Get the jump on the competition by having one of the first new home offerings of the early buying season, before the supply of offerings increases. These rewards can compensate for the rigors of a cold-weather start.

Excavate the foundation a day before the permit is ready. If plans are not finalized, consider a foundation-only permit so that you can get started sooner. Mark existing cracks in city pavements and photograph them so you are not held responsible later.

Use a foundation contractor that can complete work in a couple of days.

For concrete block basements, have the block delivered right after the footing is poured. Consider that poured concrete basement walls are stronger, drier, and allow earth to be backfilled sooner. Backfilling, rough grading, and final grading are often done at an hourly rate. Don't be too impressed with a low hourly rate for this work—the productivity provided by a large, fairly new piece of equipment and a skilled operator is most important.

Use a calculator to ascertain diagonal distances that square up the foundation. Mark these on the plan in red pencil.

Check all actual footing and wall dimensions as early as possible and also check the longest wall with a jog in it (house and garage) for parallel. In some cases, it may be best to set up batter boards for long foundation walls that must be parallel.

Framing/Rough Carpentry

Tilt-up framing saves at least 10 percent of the labor costs of traditional framing and can result in high quality work. Tilt-up framing involves building complete lengths of, say, second-floor walls on the flat floor deck, including sheathing, windows, overhang soffit and fascia or rake, gable peaks with end trusses, and sometimes siding. The entire wall is then tilted up with hand-powered jacks. Siding is usually not applied at this time because it would delay the start of rough mechanical work.

Ensure that the carpenter sub has a large enough crew—or is willing to apply at least 100 labor-hours per week—to complete the framing quickly.

Unless you have a high degree of confidence in your framing sub, visit the job site at least once each day to answer questions and check on the supplies or materials. The lead carpenter should have a copy of the detailed lumber list. Stay out of the way and try to do most of your checking at the end of each day after the carpenters have left. Then you can find problems before the work is too far along. On one occasion, I had a sub whose work was so bad that I had to terminate his contract, pay him off, and have another carpenter sub finish the work. It would have been too risky to have the first sub complete the framing. I believe strongly in maintaining a certain degree of quality, and structural safety, at all costs.

Check all dimensions and plumb walls with a four-foot or six-foot level, especially those walls that will receive wall cabinets.

Make sure the kitchen sink window will be centered between future wall cabinets.

Open and close all windows before the siding and insulation work begins.

Correct any problem yourself that requires only a few minutes of time. Leave a conspicuous note for the lead carpenter regarding any problem that he should be aware of in the early morning.

Record all unresolved problems and design change ideas in your job notebook.

Communicate the heights of all door headers above the foundation wall in the garage.

The framing lumber package can represent 10 to 15 percent of all building costs. To cut losses resulting from theft and damage, order your materials in two or three deliveries over the course of framing work and cover the materials with plastic tarps. Avoid exposure of a large lumber supply over a weekend and store windows and doors in a trailer, if possible.

Inspect material deliveries as soon as possible so that work is not delayed because of a lack of material.

Set aside lumber to be returned because of flaws or oversupply and list these items in your job notebook.

Roof trusses and windows should be on site soon after carpentry begins. You may need to make a quick trip to the lumber yard for joists, studs, or plates that are missing. An accurate lumber list (see Chapter 6) helps to avoid such errands.

Watch the size and spacing of nails and the quality of nails exposed to the weather.

Construction adhesive should be applied to the tongue-and-groove edges of plywood floors as well as to the joists.

Be sure exterior walls receive enough wind bracing.

Ensure that doubled joists and door/window headers are nailed close enough to act as a beam when spaced where plumbing lines pass through.

After the carpenters leave, I improve the wind tightness of the home by filling in between the subsill and the window sill with one-inch scraps, plumber's oakum, and butyl caulk. Butyl caulk can also be used to fill any holes in sheathing, and a continuous bead can be laid along the inside of exterior wall floor plates and any other possible air-leakage joints.

The better framing subs keep the job site neat by throwing lumber scraps in one pile and banding straps and cardboard in another. The material supply pile should look fairly well organized. If your subs don't do this, a little work on your part will give observers the impression of a well-organized, competent operation. Every Friday evening or Saturday, sweep out the house interior. This will create a favorable impression with neighbors or potential buyers who happen to stop in over the weekend. You will also be letting your framers know something about the pride in work that you favor.

Mechanical Work

Bring in the plumber early, even during the carpenter's roof sheathing work if possible.

Don't forget to have your plumber expedite the delivery of large fiberglass tub and shower modules early enough to avoid knocking out studs to set them in their respective locations. Your carpenter can set these modules and frame around and over them.

Air- or electric-powered spades can hasten the installation of waste piping that runs through stiff clay under a basement floor.

If you will be using rain gutters with flanges that extend over roof plywood, schedule gutter installation for as soon as rough carpenters finish with roof sheathing and fascia/soffit work.

Record locations of all warm-air or cold-air return outlets so you can expose them should they accidentally be covered by sheetrock.

Provide a little more than adequate attic ventilation to prevent moisture damage to the insulation.

If plumbing lines run through a drop ceiling on an exterior wall in a cold climate, provide a vent grille that allows some warm room air to surround pipes.

Some sound-deadening insulation should be placed around pipes that cross first-floor walls and ceilings.

Protect the finish on the fiberglass tub and shower modules during construction.

Use plenty of flat steel pipe protectors to prevent drywall nails or screws from penetrating pipes.

Expedite all rough mechanical inspections as soon as possible so insulation and drywall work can begin.

Roofing, Siding, Insulation, Drywall, and Flat Concrete

Schedule a two-person (or larger) roofing crew right after the completion of framing or rain gutters.

Horizontal lap siding looks professional when butt edges are even with window sills and heads and with overhang bottoms. This skill in the layout of siding courses is evident in fine older homes.

Be careful to avoid a slow-working drywall contractor. He or she should not tie up your job for more than one or two weeks.

Don't allow a horizontal joint over a second-floor joist in a stairwell.

Try to schedule flat concrete work prior to drywall and soon after rough plumbing and roofing. The garage floor could be installed before rough carpentry begins.

As you visit the job site, note any invoices for material deliveries lying around. You may need lien waivers from these supply houses to satisfy a picky title company and you'll want to be sure these suppliers are being paid by your subs or by you.

Finish Trades

About this time, the home should be locked up. Avoid having to hide a key for your subs by using a combination lockbox or a master key.

Spray paint all drywall along with the texturing process or right after this process.

Correct floor squeaks and install floor underlayment so that cabinets can be set and measurements taken for the shop work on countertops. Then set the pre-hung doors and install casings and trim while waiting for countertop installation.

Wood trim can be stained, sealed, and sanded before cutting and mounting by the carpenter. To speed up the wood stain/varnish operation, I have removed the wood window sash during drywall work and taken the sash to another location for stain/seal/varnish work.

To ease sash operation, you can sand all glide rails clean and then apply hard automobile wax.

Closet interiors should be sealed only—no stain or varnish.

The varnish coat should be done when the carpenter is gone and the dust has been cleaned up.

Don't use a slow-moving painting sub for wood finishing work.

Consider veneered trim instead of solid oak.

Closet interiors that have cased door openings and are not walk-ins don't require mitered joints; a post-and-beam style will do.

Shoe molding is needed only around cabinet bases. Base can be nailed after vinyl or tile floors are installed.

Use finish hardware that mounts fast.

Avoid the cheap look of rail balusters that are spaced too widely. Install your newels and balusters so that they feel solid when a buyer tries to shake the railing.

Detail with a router the edges of oak boards used as wall caps and fireplace surrounds.

You may be able to build the basement stairs before the drywallers leave—another time-saver.

Let your vinyl installer choose the underlayment and fastening method—he or she wants the work to be trouble-free.

The dishwasher you select can be just one step up from the bottom of a well-known line. People appreciate not having too many buttons to deal with. Add extra insulation around the dishwasher for quieter operation.

Be sure your interior colors are coordinated and currently popular (but not trendy), and can blend with most furnishings.

Exterior decks, interior mock beam ceilings, and crown moldings can often be omitted until a buyer is found. Then you may be able to charge a good price for them.

Depending on the market and price of the home, you may be able to omit jambs and casings from sliding closet door openings.

Critical Path and Calendar Scheduling

Critical path scheduling is quite prevalent in large commercial construction projects but not generally in small home building. This method identifies all phases or tasks that are part of the "critical path" — jobs that cannot be started until the previous job is complete. For instance, rough framing cannot begin until the foundation is complete. Adding up the time necessary to complete all the critical path jobs can give you an idea of the minimum time needed to complete the home.

Non-critical path jobs can be undertaken during the work on one or more critical path jobs. For example, siding can be applied during framing, during rough mechanicals, or during drywall. If you understand this system, you can find ways to shorten your overall building time. You may be able to cut the time by 50 percent, but you still have to depend on the best service from all your subs and suppliers.

The calendar or bar chart scheduling method is most prevalent in home construction. A large 11″ x 17″ desk pad calendar can be used, with tasks written across the date blocks. Critical path knowledge can be applied here, but allow for some flexibility, changes, and erasures. You can lay out the schedule in a way that will remind you to order items with enough lead time.

If you are building two homes at the same time, you will need a second calendar. You could also divide each date block in one calendar into two parts.

Items of work that need attention today or tomorrow can be also listed on a daily desk calendar and checked off as the day progresses.

Saving Total Construction Time

Well-organized builders can complete a home in 65 to 75 percent of what is considered the normal time span for their locality. Being able to build a home in 90 calendar days increases your annual income, partly because every day saved from the start-to-sale/closing cycle can reduce financing costs by about $25. The greatest benefit, however, is being able to build 20 to 30 percent more housing each year.

You could try to include a liquidated damage clause in some subcontracts to penalize a sub for late completion of his work. This clause is rarely used, however.

Keeping a Job Notebook

I carry a small three-ring binder everywhere. Each job has a separate section, identified with the address, legal description, building inspector's phone number, and permit number. Differences between benchmarks and footing bottoms, for excavations and sewer drainage, are recorded here. Unfinished work and work that needs correction are listed and checked off as they are completed.

You can also use a job notebook to write down ideas for building the same design again — changes in material lists, notes of actual quantities and colors of materials used, labor hours for various trades, and design changes to consider.

The layout of forced-air heating ducts and outlets, together with the location of downspouts and plumbing soil pipes, could be useful information to record in the job notebook.

You can also use the notebook to make up punch lists.

A similar-sized calendar book, with a full day on each page, is useful for recording what's going on and can serve as a field extension of your office calendar and scheduling chart.

Hiring Construction Management

I am generally at the job site for more hours of the week than most builders—this enables me to achieve a good level of quality work. At some point, you may want to hire someone to help with these duties.

You can hire construction management on an hourly, percentage, or flat-fee basis. Hourly fees might be $30 to $50. Percentage fees might be 3 to 5 percent of the total building cost, and flat fees can range from $2,500 to $5,000 or more. In general, construction management costs should not exceed 5 percent of the total building cost.

Why would a professional small builder want to hire a construction manager? The most likely reason may be that the builder is new to the business and needs to get acquainted with subs and local practices. Working in a new location, with a different method or style of construction, even a well-experienced builder would be wise to get local help. Also, considering all the tasks required of the spec builder, from site and market research to sale/closing, the construction management task is probably the most frustrating and life-consuming. You may be involved in this work as early as 5:30 a.m. and as late as 11 p.m.—not necessarily a continuous day, but a long day in any case.

Construction management is one of the first tasks hired out when a builder becomes more than just a one-man operation. Even if your business is too small to afford even a part-time or temporary expediter, the cost may be worthwhile when you consider the improvement it can bring to your day-to-day life. Weigh the cost of such assistance against the benefits to your health, family life, level of stress, and so on.

A private home inspector, an older, more experienced carpenter, or a small custom builder can serve as your expediter, at least part time. Be sure you are protected with insurance, whether it's the expediter's or your own. A carpenter could also do smaller carpentry jobs on each home. Payment could be either a lump sum for the whole house or an hourly fee for service provided for just part of the construction cycle.

Paying Bills

Prompt payment of bills, especially to subcontractors, is the best way to ensure good service. Some very successful builders go so far as to pay subs weekly instead of monthly, or immediately upon completion of work. If the job is not fully completed, be careful not to pay for more than 85 percent of the work that is completed at time of payment. You need to retain at least 15 percent to ensure their completion of the job, especially if you suspect that you have an unreliable sub. Many a new builder has been stung by a carpenter who demanded one-third to one-half of his money during the first or second day on the job and never returned after cashing the check.

Sometimes a sub will offer a 2 to 5 percent (or more) discount for prompt payment after completion, or for weekly payments. If the sub does not offer a discount, ask about it. If you're not able to get a discount, state that good service and workmanship is expected in exchange for prompt payment. If you do someone a favor, often he or she will return a little something extra in service or workmanship.

Suppliers often offer discounts of one to five percent for prompt monthly payments of their bills. When multiplied by 12 months, these discounts yield 12 to 60 percent annually. Pay promptly—where can you get a better rate of return for your money?

The Certificate of Occupancy

If you have done a good job as a business manager and builder, you should have a sale agreement by the time the certificate of occupancy is granted. Time is often precious at this point— you should try to be at the home when the final inspection is made so that any problem can be dealt with immediately. The certificate of occupancy for the new home is granted based on the completion of a building that is safe for occupancy and that fully satisfies the building code. Pick up the certificate of occupancy from the building department as soon as it is ready and inform the buyer, lender, and title company of this.

Summary

As stated at the opening of this chapter, scheduling and supervision are probably the most trying aspects of building. There are personal relationships and communication to consider, as well as a vast array of more technical scheduling and supervision considerations in every category of construction. Throughout the project you must also keep an eye on the calendar and on your incoming invoices.

Chapter 9 concerns marketing issues that you will encounter both before and after the home is complete—advertising, pricing, negotiations, relationships with brokers, and the sale itself.

Key Points
- Apply for utility services either before or during your application for a building permit.
- Rather than perform construction work yourself, you should do market research, search for the next building site, increase subcontractor and supplier sources, and supervise construction.
- Be sure to discuss your workmanship standards with each new sub.
- Keep in mind that certain materials must be ordered well in advance of the time of their actual delivery to the site.
- Calendar or bar chart scheduling is most prevalent in home construction; lay out the schedule in such a way that will remind you to order materials with enough lead time.

- Keep a job notebook for each project.
- Hiring construction management can make a great improvement in your day-to-day life. Construction management costs should not exceed 5% of the total building cost.
- Prompt payment of bills to subs and suppliers is the best way to ensure good service—and perhaps obtain discounts.
- Try to be present during the final inspection so that any problem can be dealt with immediately.

Chapter 9
Marketing

Marketing, for a spec home builder, encompasses a variety of processes—advertising and signage, pricing and negotiations, dealing with real estate brokers (or deciding not to), the offer to purchase, and more. Once you have designed and started to build a spec home, you must begin to plan a marketing strategy.

Advertising

Your advertising plan should be established early in the construction stage. If you have built the design before, most of the work will have been done already. You need to decide at which stages of construction you will advertise, hold open houses, or list the home with a broker—all of these steps are part of your marketing plan. Remember, poor or slow sales are the major downfall of the small builder, so some planning in terms of marketing is time well spent.

The total cost of all advertising, if you are able to sell your home without a broker, should run no more than 1 percent to 2 percent of the home sale price. More than 3 percent is definitely too much.

Newspaper Advertising

Newspaper advertising can begin as soon as the sheetrock is being installed. The best choice is either the most popular metropolitan newspaper and/or a popular large suburban paper. A small creative advertisement works better than a large unimaginative one.

You might place your ad in the real estate classified section of a large metropolitan paper. Run the ad on several Sundays or throughout the week. The ad should cover these points:

- The location (street address and directions, if necessary)
- Open house time, if any
- Number of bedrooms and baths
- Description as one- or two-story home
- Some unique feature(s) such as a special site, two-story foyer, three-car garage—whatever sets it apart from the competition

- The price
- Your phone number

The word "Builder" before the phone number attracts those buyers who are aware of the advantages of dealing with the builder.

Don't forget to mention that the house is brand new. Don't make any overstatements in the ad—it is better that the prospects be pleasantly surprised rather than disappointed when they see the home. Do set a tone in the ad that makes prospects want to call. If the location is special, be sure to mention it. The ad should not be too lengthy—its purpose is simply to elicit a phone call or a visit. If you advertise in a suburban paper, you may be able to afford a small display ad instead of a classified ad.

If you are building at least three or four spec homes per year, you might run a small, continuous classified ad. Here you can mention new homes under construction in a general area, the type of homes, and their sizes and price range. In this way you can pick up prospects who can wait several months before buying. This is a way to benefit from the cumulative effect of continuous advertising.

Your ad for a specific home should not run for more than two or three weeks or it will become stale. Have a new and different ad ready. Remember the segments of the market that you decided to reach when you first planned this home (see Chapter 3). What are they looking for? What papers do they read? Target your marketing to them. Study the ads of your competition carefully.

See Figure 9.1 for an example of a newspaper classified advertisement for a home built by my company in the late 1980s.

Brochures

You should create an information sheet about your home that you can hand out to prospective buyers and brokers; something that compares favorably with the model sales brochures that are offered by larger builders. This handout could be as large as 11″ x 17″, folded in half so that it is, in effect, a four-page brochure. Reduced-size artist renderings and floor plans, together with a list of quality features and specifications to satisfy most prospects' or

GRAFTON: New duplex, 860 & 864 Maple St. Two-story town homes—1,300 square feet on each side. 3 bedrooms, 1-1/2 baths each. Wood decks, 2 attached garages. Single for tenant, double for owner. $129,800. Ridgeline Homes, 555-1234

Figure 9.1 Sample Classified Advertisement

brokers' questions, can be included in the handout. Be sure to point out any special advantages of the location or subdivision.

An information sheet including a floor plan was shown in Chapter 5. A two-page sales brochure that I used to sell my own home appears in Figure 9.2. Several photos could be added to the brochure to illustrate the home's features.

If you are able to repeat the same home design several times, you can afford to develop a fine brochure, leaving space to insert descriptions of the varying locations. These brochures can be left out on kitchen counters and placed in weatherproof boxes near your job sign (signage is discussed later in this chapter).

On the back page of the brochure, or in a separate brochure, you might consider writing a brief public relations story of your business—your background, years of experience, the focus and philosophy of the business (e.g. "producing the most home for the least cost" or "limiting production to five homes per year in order to maintain quality").

The Home

Don't forget that your greatest, most effective advertisement is the house itself. If you have built in an active subdivision where several other builders are producing homes, your product will bring more response than any ad. You will have a self-advertising location and will benefit from the advertising and traffic of your competitors.

Open House

As soon as the interior of the home has drywall and some interior woodwork or cabinets installed, you can consider an open house for one or two Sunday afternoons. A thorough description of the procedures involved in conducting an open house could comprise the bulk of this book. Any "for sale by owner" guidebook that you can find at a bookstore will contain helpful advice. You might also gain an education by observing open houses held by real estate brokers.

Signage

Your combined business/for-sale sign should be posted at the job site as soon as construction begins. The sign should be professional quality, about five square feet in size. Include your business name and phone number(s), and call attention to the fact that the home is being built for sale. This sign will also help subs and suppliers locate your job.

If you think that prospects might need help locating your home, or if you just want to increase drive-by traffic, consider posting small paper directional signs on trees and power poles at nearby intersections and along busy roads. Just your business name, phone number, and/or "new home," together with a distinct directional arrow, will steer people to your offering. In any event, these directional signs can really increase your market exposure.

As the home is nearing completion, display some 3″ x 5″ cards at various points in the home that call out features or quality items that are not readily apparent. Some examples are: "8 inch concrete wall with 1 inch styrofoam

(Optional Photo)

Home for Sale: $165,000

3 bedrooms, 2-1/2 baths, 2,200 sq. ft.
Location: 123 Smith Drive

Land and Views: .94 acre lot (202' x 202'). Rear (south) of lot is thick woods as is the west side of lot and portion of roadside area. During warm months, deck and rear yard are very private. Views of golf course from west side of home and of park-like three-acre homesite to south during colder months. Lawn area is approximately 1/4 acre. Home is set back over 75 feet from front lot line. Asphalt drive has three-car guest parking area. Municipal sewer. Excellent well produces 10 gallons per minute. Taxes (1989): $3,282.

General Notes: Cape Cod style, with two (2) gables and bay window on front elevation. Five (5) small skylights illuminate foyer, east bedroom, and master bath. All upper window sashes are divided lites. Gray-black asphalt shingle roof, white trim, almond insulated aluminum siding, and brick to first-floor window sills on all sides of home. Wide covered entry, porch with railing. Rear of house faces directly south and has a large wood deck with bench seats.

Interior: Approximately 2,200 square feet of living area. The interior is light and airy as all rooms have windows on two (2) walls whenever possible. First-floor laundry/mud room adjoins garage entry. Very livable floor plan. Oak doors and oak colonial trim. No-wax vinyl floors, nylon beige carpets. Colored plumbing fixtures.

(Front of Brochure)

First Floor

- *First-floor Foyer:* Classic ceramic tile entry floor. Vaulted ceiling to overlook and platform on second floor. Straight-ahead view to patio door and deck.
- *Kitchen-Dinette* (11-1/2' x 21'): Quite large. U-shaped work area. Raised panel oak cabinets. Cast iron sink under window. Disposal, dishwasher, self-cleaning oven. Pantry closet. Patio door in dinette leads to deck.
- *Family Room* (13' x 17'): In view of dinette/kitchen with capped wall separation. Brick fireplace with oak mantle and custom oak surround. Crown molding.
- *Living Room* (13' x 19-1/2'): Near foyer. Features include bay window and crown molding.
- *Dining Room* (13' x 12'): Features include two (2) windows and wallpaper crown trim.
- *Powder Room:* Off foyer and living room hall.

Second Floor

- *Master Bedroom* (13' x 13'+): Has 5-3/4' x 8' alcove for sitting area off main bedroom area. Walk-in closet, compartmented. Master bath has 5' vanity, fiberglass shower stall with glass doors, and skylight.
- *Bedrooms 2 & 3:* Measure 10' x 15' and 10-1/2' x 17', both with ample closets.
- *Main Bath:* 4' vanity. Fiberglass tub/shower.

Basement

11-course painted block. Automatic water softener and laundry tub.

Garage

2-1/2 car; 20' x 24'. Overhead door operator and service door.

Energy Features: Insulated foundation walls. Home exceeds code requirements for heat loss. Walls= 22-1/2 total R-value. Ceilings are R=38. Rear of home and much glass faces directly south. Gas furnace is one year old, high efficiency (92%). 2-1/2 ton central air conditioning. Automatic attic fan lowers need for air conditioning. Gas 40-gallon water heater is efficient sub-chamber A.O. Smith. Home was caulked at roughing stage for extra wind-tightness.

Total energy use including central air for the 12 months preceding May 1990 are:

Electric	$444.38
Gas	467.65
Total	$912.03

(Back of Brochure)

Figure 9.2 Sales Brochure for a Particular Home

insulation on exterior;" "HUD approved, washable wall paint throughout;" "high R-value, triple-pane windows;" "gas fireplace;" "200 amp. electric service;" and "attic exhaust fan." These little information cards, placed on walls, windows, counters, etc., will be appreciated by both prospects and brokers. If your roofing has a longer than normal manufacturer's warranty, mention this fact both in your brochure and on an information card.

Pricing and Negotiations

During the drywall stage of construction, go over the most recent actual and estimated costs. Re-examine the price competition from both new and nearly-new homes. Try to see these other offerings through the eyes of a buyer.

Setting a Price

Get a recent copy of the multiple listing catalog from your broker contact— the one who will get your listing should you fail to find a buyer on your own. Review the competition in your area and price range, and check on recent sales and asking prices in another section of the catalog. Write down the information you need, such as size of home and number of bedrooms and baths. Then drive past these homes. Maybe you can visit an open house. You should investigate the multiple listing catalog at least twice: at the time of lot purchase/house design and at the time you finalize your asking price.

New homes often sell for their asking prices during good times, but be prepared for lower offers during "normal" times. You really need to set three prices: 1) your asking price; 2) as your most private information, a price that you will be satisfied with if negotiation is necessary; and 3) a rock-bottom price for a difficult situation—a price that you cannot lower any further.

Your pricing should consider the normal markup over costs, as discussed in Chapter 2, as well as the competition. Your asking price should meet the competition in a normal market and beat the competition in a tough market. Most sellers and many builders price their homes too high. They reason that they're going to get lower offers anyway. What usually happens is that prospective buyers are put off from making any offers. The asking price that attracts the most offers is the price that is close to the true value. The negotiated final sale price will probably be only one to two percent below the asking price. Overpricing is one of the worst mistakes you can make.

Real Estate Brokers

Brokers may suggest a price, but they may be creating a reason for listing with them by creating false hopes with a price that is a bit high. Remember, most broker clients are living in their homes and can afford to wait months for a sale. You may want to take a more aggressive sales approach than the average broker would. The builder-broker relationship is discussed in more detail later in this chapter.

The general public is now more aware of negotiating possibilities in home purchases. Your buyer may be represented by a "buyer's broker" who will really work on your price—that's one of the things this type of broker is hired to do. Prepare yourself by studying a book or tape on the subject of negotiation. See the Resources Appendix for some titles.

Negotiating Options and Upgrades

Sometimes buyers try to obtain a much lower price indirectly, by offering to pay the asking price after a number of costly options and upgrades are added. The upgrades might include something like central air conditioning; a larger carpet allowance; the finish of a basement room; or the addition of crown moldings throughout the house. You will be prepared to deal with this if you have priced out some common options beforehand. You may have to throw in something for free. Just be sure you don't end up below an acceptable price level. Also, these changes should not cause a delay in the sale closing.

Some buyers want to reinvest all the sale proceeds from their last home to avoid a capital gains tax; for this reason, it is to their advantage to get free upgrades rather than a lower price.

When negotiating only about price, if you reach an impasse, consider throwing in an item that the buyer values highly but that is available at low cost to you. For example, you might offer to include a small set of bookshelves or a microwave oven.

Marketing: Timing and Exposure

Although you would like to sell your spec home as quickly as possible, you should be aware of the dangers of bringing a buyer "on board" at the earlier stages of construction.

Timing

You can avoid some problems by delaying the showing of your product to buyers until the drywall has been installed and painted. If you show the home at earlier stages, the prospective buyer will often want to make major disruptive changes to your plan, such as moving walls or windows. Many of these changes are attractive only to that person, not to the broad market. Even if you are well compensated for these changes, the sale may not go through and you'll have a "customized" house to try to sell to the general market.

Another reason to wait is that the interior of the home will look more spacious and inviting when stud walls are covered with sheetrock and light reflective paint. The installation of some cabinets or other woodwork will give buyers a feel for final quality.

There is one period of the year when home sales are always slow—between mid-November and early January. Try to avoid bringing a home to market at that time.

Exposure

The broader the exposure, the quicker the sale. Sometimes just a conversation with a neighbor does wonders (see the case study below). No matter how hard you may try—using newspapers, directional signs, conversations, supermarket and employer bulletin boards—the greatest exposure will come from your product's listing in the realtor's multi-listing book that is issued every two weeks.

Case Study:
Casual Conversations Can Yield Surprising Leads

My first sale came through a neighbor who had just had a home built next to the one I was building. I invited him to inspect the house as it neared completion. He liked it and said he might know someone who would be interested. A week later, his barber came out and bought the home.

Broker Contacts

If you have produced a desirable home and offered it at a good price, brokers will be coming to you and calling constantly. They will often have buyers in tow. They might also call asking if you will cooperate or co-broke with brokers, sign a short-term exclusive listing agreement, or agree to a one-party (prospective buyer) listing. While it's still early in the game, you are still trying to sell the home on your own so you can afford to resist their efforts to obtain a full commission. You should be able to pay no more than half of the full commission for the individual prospective buyers they bring by, avoiding a broad exclusive listing. That can be used later if necessary. When the market is hot, why pay for any kind of brokerage service if you can get your price without it?

Although you may want to sell your house without a broker, keep in mind that brokers are the source of 50 percent to 75 percent of buyers for the small builder—so you will undoubtedly need to enlist their services at some time. Brokers have been involved in about half of all my home sales. Buyers who come with a broker are less likely to distrust the builder. On average, a broker will usually be able to get 3 percent more for the home than an owner or builder can. But this 3 percent gap can be narrowed to almost zero as a builder becomes more sophisticated in dealing directly with buyers. In other words, the sophisticated seller can obtain a price that is equal to what the broker can obtain.

When dealing directly with prospective buyers, never undercut the price that brokers are quoting. As soon as word of double dealing gets out, brokers will avoid you like the plague. Remember, you will surely need a broker at some point in the future. Sometimes builders/sellers try to hide their price undercutting by throwing in a subtle upgrade to clinch the deal. Word of this type of dealing eventually gets around, too.

Another advantage to using brokers is that the prospects are usually more qualified to buy than the ones you will meet directly, and of course, your product will be shown much more often.

Inform the broker fully about your product but don't divulge any information about your financial situation, gross profit margins, or any anxiety over selling. A rumor could spread that you're ripe for a low offer and a quick, easy commission. Emphasize the unique and hidden quality features to brokers. A hidden feature might be something like a roofing material that offers a longer warranty period or a superior-quality adhesive—qualities that are not obvious to the general public. You can acquaint a lot of brokers with your product if you hold an open house for brokers (perhaps with coffee and donuts) on the weekday on which they all go around to see their new listings. You can invite brokers to your open house simply by phoning them.

If your efforts and those of one-shot brokers haven't produced a sale, it's time to list your home with someone who can provide multi-listing coverage at a competitive commission. Do this a few weeks before the completion of the home.

The Brokerage Industry

A little background on the brokerage industry is appropriate here. Many decades ago, the selling of real estate was handled by small offices—often insurance agencies—who did not share their listings with other offices. New-home buyers usually dealt directly with the builder. As a national group, brokers and builders were in the same position in their dealings with buyers. Brokers eventually created their own national organization—with local boards, a system of setting fees, and sophisticated public relations. A powerful brokerage industry developed with top to bottom controls.

Builders take a great deal of risk with costs, weather conditions, and markets to produce housing. The competition puts great demands on their creativity and expertise in many aspects of their endeavors. In the end, brokers can receive a fixed fee from this activity as well as from resales, to produce profits that may be greater over time than the builder's. Proof of this greater profit for less risk can be observed by noting that when large nationwide securities or retail corporations diversify into the housing industry, they buy up a brokerage business instead of a building business. Brokerage tends to offer more profit for less risk. Based on risk alone, the builder should really receive the larger reward. To quote Donald P. Grant, a professor of architecture, "Productive behavior is simply not what this society rewards most highly, manipulative behavior is."

While it is true that the brokerage industry benefits consumers by providing a good educational system and keeping abreast of current legal issues, the best thing that has developed for sellers and buyers is the sharing of all listings through multiple listing services. This part of their service is well organized.

Because real estate salespeople work on commission only, real estate firms will typically have a large number of agents. With all these salespeople to support, a large inventory of homes is needed; because of this, the focus of the most talented people in a firm may shift from selling homes to listing homes. The end result is an overstaffed industry claiming that they need fee rates of 6 or 7 percent to survive. It is interesting to note that "estate agents," as they are called in England, provide brokerage services there for a 2 percent fee.

Anyone who places a sign or advertisement to sell a home independently knows that during the first week or two, he or she will be approached by many real estate people. Because there are so many real estate firms in a given area, there is a lot of competition to sell a new house that becomes available. One of the broker's jobs is to convince buyers not to go looking for housing without a broker. Buyers who would otherwise look at for-sale-by-owner (FSBO) homes as well as listed properties often opt for the ease and comfort of looking with a broker. These buyers are no longer available to deal with the builder directly.

It could be argued that America might be better off with fewer people in the real estate business. A smaller number of efficient people could concentrate on getting property sold instead of competing with each other for listings, and brokerage fees might be 25 percent less. Just as much, if not more, property could be sold in such an arrangement, and the remaining salespeople could have significant incomes. Unfortunately, this scenario is unlikely to occur, since the real estate business has become a major industry, and so many people are attracted to its profit potential.

Commission Percentages

About 50 percent of the broker's commission, whether for listing or for selling, goes to his or her employer. Often there is also a 50/50 split between the listing broker and the selling broker. In some locations, 60 percent of the total 6 percent commission goes to the lister and his or her firm and 40 percent goes to the seller and his or her firm. If you look at a multi-listing catalog, you'll see a small number in a box in the lower corner of each listing. This is the selling commission; this number lets the salesperson know exactly what's in it for him or her before showing any specific listing. Unfortunately, some salespeople will avoid showing a listing that offers anything less than the normal rate.

When the listing commission is 3.6 percent and the selling portion is 2.4 percent, it's no wonder that the most experienced brokers concentrate on listing instead of selling—it pays more. In an old real estate textbook, I found an example of commission splitting that was 10 percent for listing and 90 percent for selling.

The national range for full-service commissions for selling homes is about 6 percent to 7 percent. Seven percent is a lot of money for the general public and very expensive for a builder. In some parts of the country, brokers charge 7 percent for all price ranges, while a thousand miles away, in an equally large metropolitan area, brokers charge 7 percent only on the first $100,000 of sale and 3.5 percent after that. According to the latter arrangement, the sale of a $200,000 home would cost $10,500 in commission. The straight 7 percent plan would cost $14,000, and a 6 percent commission would cost $12,000.

In my home state, there are two distinct and separate resort areas that attract both vacation-home buyers and retirees. The brokers in one resort area charge 6 percent while brokers in the other resort area charge 10 percent. Since the two areas are only a hundred miles apart, it appears that these fees are not based solely on the costs of doing business.

Negotiating Commissions

Real estate commissions in general are presented to the public as if they are non-negotiable; a broker can offer dozens of reasons why your home cannot be sold for a smaller fee. It is important for the builder to realize that fees are negotiable. Some brokers have a special rate for builders, usually one point less than the fee for the general public. That is 5 percent instead of 6 percent, or 6 percent instead of 7 percent. Can brokers afford to work for less, and will they? More on this later, in the "Listing Commissions vs. Selling Commissions" discussion.

Here are two fairly recent innovations in real estate office setups that might offer the service that a builder needs, for less cost. There are some nationally franchised offices in which individual brokers pay a high price for office space and other services, including ads, but do not split commissions in any appreciable way with the office. There are also franchises that offer no sales personnel, but assist sellers with forms, signs, ads, and so on. Of course, multi-listing is a must and you may be able to get it for less with either type of operation.

Personalities

The real estate business attracts some fiercely competitive people — even some with a lack of ethics as well as some who use the occupation as kind of a status hobby. There are, of course, some really fine people out there. You must be selective in your choice of a listing broker. Your ultimate selling broker will probably be someone you have never met or heard of before.

The right to sell the property of another is based on the old legal principles of agency in which the agent should always act in a way that will serve his principal best, even if it does not serve the agent well. The agent's compensation is predetermined and limited to that. Despite all the education and examinations required, this basic agency principle is the one that some brokers either don't fully understand or ignore.

Case Studies:
Knowledge is Important When Dealing with Brokers

During one sale negotiation (offer, counter offer, new offer) the selling broker refused to tell me what amount the buyers had told her was the maximum amount they intended to pay. This amount was $2,000 over their second offer. This broker did not understand that I was her principal, and that her allegiance was strictly to me. She consulted with her office manager, who confirmed that I was correct. After learning of this figure, we added $500 to it as our counter offer and it was accepted.

On another occasion, the listing/selling broker did not understand the basics of contract law. He thought we could raise the low offering price without the risk of having the buyer back away and get his deposit back. The point here is that while you are paying dearly for a professional service, you may be getting very incompetent service. Had I not been fairly well acquainted with real estate law myself, I may have lost control over situations like this. Knowledge is power!

The Right Broker

What kind of salesperson makes the best listing agent for the builder? Remember that the lister will be the person that selling brokers will call to ask questions and get directions to the property. In all cases, the lister should be able to describe your product intelligently and enthusiastically to the selling brokers that call, and inform them of details in the offer to purchase that are unique and important to the builder. The listing broker should be constantly available to speak with selling brokers and to bring offers to you promptly. If commission rates are equal, go with a lister who is highly regarded by his or her peers, one that selling brokers can easily work with.

Your lister should genuinely like your product. This confidence in your work will be projected to selling brokers and then to buyers. You don't need the type of lister who has talent for the prodding, educating, and hand-holding required for dealing with a listing from the average home owner.

Keep in mind that the lister will most likely *not* be the person who actually sells your home. In my experience, the listing agent has been the selling broker less than 10 percent of the time.

If you have not had good luck in selling your homes yourself or you don't like dealing with buyers, list every home with your favorite low-cost lister as soon as it is being drywalled. In many metropolitan areas, the transferee market is large. It is almost impossible to reach these transferees without a broker. They tend to buy new or nearly new homes and rely on brokers both to apprise them of good locations and to expose them to a maximum number of choices in their very limited searching time.

The Listing Contract

The listing contract should not only spell out the total fee percentage, but also specify exactly the percentage fee that the selling broker and his or her firm will receive. More on this later, in "Listing Commissions vs. Selling Commissions."

Try to list the home for just 60 days. That will cause your listing broker to get busy quickly.

Make sure the lister writes down all the non-obvious special features. The listing contract should include words of warranty and specifications for uncompleted work at the time of offer, which should be part of all offers. After you have listed, request that the lister furnish you with computer printouts and the multi-listing catalog so you can check the accuracy of information.

In general, your product should elicit an acceptable offer within 30 days with a multi-listing broker unless the market is bad or you have not done your job as a skilled spec builder and businessperson.

Listing Commissions vs. Selling Commissions

You should not think about the real estate commission without considering its two parts: listing commission and selling commission.

Consider the selling commission first. This commission offers the least opportunity for cutting back. Consider the sale of new homes by large tract builders. Their own salespeople have furnished models, an inventory of lots, and a few completed homes ready for occupancy. Their commission is usually in the 2 to 2-1/2 percent range, and sometimes as low as 1-1/4 percent. The tract builder often cooperates with brokers all over the area by offering 2 to 2-1/2 percent to each broker who brings a qualified buyer to the model home center. The builder's own salespeople take over at that point and are compensated at their usual percentage.

Examine your local multi-listing catalog thoroughly for a comparison of quoted commissions for single-family homes. Most rates will be the same, but a few may be slightly less and a few others may be quite a bit less. Try to determine which of these lower-fee listings are new construction. Other builders may be able to pay a lower-than-normal selling commission that still attracts brokers who are working with new home buyers. Selling commissions that are too low, however, will be ignored by most salespeople. For example, if 7 percent is the total full commission with a 50/50 split, you may see some builders whose listings offer a 2.5 percent or 3 percent selling commission instead of the normal 3.5 percent. In our area, with a 60/40 split, the normal selling commission is 2.4 percent but some builder products are offered at 2 percent. With a little research, you should be able to determine the lowest cost-effective selling commission for a new home.

My experience with listing commissions has varied from 1 percent to 3.6 percent, or from $1,500 to $5,400 on a $150,000 sale. This area deserves some real analysis.

Salespeople can be involved in a fair amount of work as listing agents to the general public. First, there is the tremendous amount of time spent looking for listings and competing against other brokers. Research, strategy, and negotiation go into setting a price on the home and in drafting the listing contract. It may require extra time to unearth the required multi-listing information from local officials, surveyors, etc. During the listing period, calling for showing appointments, reporting back on showings, and answering calls from the anxious owner can eat up a great deal of time. Finally, if the price hasn't been set too high, an offer will be received. Getting the owner's acceptance can take hours or even days.

A good relationship between the spec builder and the broker eliminates most of the typical listing time and all of the advertising costs. The broker doesn't have to chase after listings—the builder returns to the same lister each time multi-listing brokerage is needed. The efficient builder has all of the necessary listing and offering information ready, including the price. The listing agreement can be finished in half an hour. There is no need to call for appointments or report back, no open houses, and no hand-holding for an anxious seller. The builder or lister installs a lock box at the front door and selling agents let themselves in. Offers presented are dealt with rather quickly. No advertising is required—the multi-listing is enough. Lastly, the professional spec builder is more motivated to conclude a sale than the average homeowner would be, because the builder is actually losing money each extra day that the house stays on the market.

Under the above circumstances, it is easy to see the justification for cutting normal listing commissions by 50 to 70 percent. Of course, you must first find a broker who is willing and able to do this.

Case Study:
It is Worthwhile to Search for a Low-Cost Broker

When I first obtained a multi-listing listing at 5 percent total in a 6 percent market, I found that both listing and selling commissions were cut back by 17 percent, to 3 percent and 2 percent. A year later I happened across a one-person brokerage firm that specialized in new construction and charged 3 percent: 1 percent for listing and 2 percent to the selling broker. The broker used the 1 percent to pay for the phone, a small office, multi-listing fees, a small box stocked with brochures outside each home, and the services of a law firm to draft deeds and closing statements. The remainder of the 1 percent provided him with a decent living. This was a rock-bottom-cost operation. While there are tradeoffs, it may be worthwhile to search for an efficient, low-cost listing broker.

Lower Broker Commissions

Imagine paying 1.5 percent to 2 percent for listing and 2 percent to 2.5 percent for selling, or a total commission of 3.5 percent to 4.5 percent for the sale of your homes. Where can you find this listing broker? Perhaps in a one-person firm like the one described above. If you can't find one, you might get together with other spec builders and create a listing potential large enough to entice a broker to set up an office. Otherwise, look for a small firm or the type of office where the individual brokers and salespeople have a great deal of autonomy. A highly regarded broker in a large firm may be able to persuade his or her employer to allow this arrangement as a separate operation. With all the licensed real estate people in this country, it should not take too long to get the important multi-listing effect at a reasonable cost.

Large, existing commercial properties are normally sold at negotiated total commissions that end up in the 2.5 percent to 4 percent range. A builder/broker arrangement that I have seen in several parts of the country involves a brokerage firm that handles all lot sales in a new subdivision, gives builders first choice on all lots (sometimes requiring the builder to purchase two or three lots at once), and, in return, maintains a listing on all homes built, but at a lower-than-market commission rate. Commission is rated on the property minus lot cost; so in the final analysis, the total commission is only 65 to 75 percent of the market rate for existing homes. Paying too much for brokerage can cut your 8 to 10 percent net profit by 25 to 33 percent. Be careful not to give away too much of your hard-earned profit.

Another strategy is to ask a full-commission broker to reduce the commission when he or she brings in a low offer in a situation where a counter offer is too risky. This is easier to do when you don't have two brokers (a lister and a seller). In a weak market, it makes sense for the builder and the broker to share the pain.

Finally, here is a tactic you might use with a broker who boasts about how fast he or she can sell and insists on a full commission. Tell the broker that each month of delay in the sale closing costs you over 1 percent in carrying costs. You will pay the full commission if a sale is consummated in, say, 45 days. Each month thereafter, insist that the commission be lowered by one point.

Builder as Licensed Broker

During all of the time that I have built homes in my state, I have held a broker's license. It has saved me some money. If you have a real estate license, it is possible to legally "co-broker" when other brokers come in with buyers. However, I have never belonged to a multi-listing service — the cost is too high for my sales volume. Also, I might not be available when selling brokers need quick answers. On one or two occasions, I saved a little on the lot purchase cost by being listed as co-broker on the broker's closing statement.

If you or your spouse can obtain a broker's license without too much time and expense, consider it. It will add a little to your income and to your business image. For a low-volume builder, however, it certainly isn't crucial.

With or Without a Broker: Some Final Advice

When a builder tries to do his or her own selling, a variety of problems can arise. Often, unqualified buyers get the builder involved in a process that leads nowhere. These buyers are usually weeded out at brokerage firms, since they are skilled at qualifying buyers.

Get to know a good, active, and reliable mortgage person who can qualify prospects for you. The brokerage community knows who these high-caliber mortgage people are. Don't forget to calculate the opportunity cost of spending time with buyers. It may be more profitable to spend your time lining up your next spec project.

The best situation is to live in a home that is a duplicate of your spec homes. Here you can show what your spec home will be like when it is finished. Your own home becomes a great marketing aid in many ways. Let the listing and selling brokers know about the availability of your "model home," should they need it to clinch the sale with a hesitant buyer.

Before your spec home is listed, you will encounter a few brokers stopping by with and without buyers along. You should provide your fact sheet to these brokers immediately, so that accurate information is conveyed to all prospective buyers.

Avoid offers that are contingent upon the sale of the buyer's present home. Get involved only with buyers who seem to have at least a 90 percent chance of being able to consummate the sale. However, there is a technique for dealing with the sale contigency problem that is covered in the next section.

A lot of lost time and uncertainty can be avoided by meeting with the buyer and selling broker to draft an offer and acceptance on the spot. Usually this is done with the salesperson's supervision broker present.

Finally, never tell any broker (or buyer) about the lowest offer you would accept. This puts you in an unnecessarily vulnerable position.

Case Study:
Selling a Home Yourself May Require Meeting "Interesting" People

In the late 1980s, I met up with a large number of unusual prospective buyers on a spec home. The first appeared right after rough carpentry and insisted we add a fourth bedroom, which was very difficult to do. Then there was a low bidder who acted ready to buy, but didn't have a firm sale on his old home. An unmarried couple qualified in front of a good loan officer, who correctly predicted that the woman would default before the closing because she was apprehensive about the stability of the relationship with her partner. Another sale was contingent upon an out-of-state closing, which dragged on until I exercised my option to void the contract. The last buyer was ready to draft an offer when his employer hinted that he could be transferred out of state within a year. By that time I was ready for a multi-listing, which produced a solid deal in a few weeks.

Approaching the Offer to Purchase

Unless you have experience selling big-ticket items, you need to learn when to be aggressive and when to be passive when talking to prospects. It is my experience that a low key, slightly detached, but helpful attitude on the seller's part works best. Be very careful about being aggressive. When prospects start to get critical about the property and its details, they are usually starting to visualize themselves living there. They may be looking for some points to justify a lower offer, or they may be genuinely concerned about the quality of some part of the home. At this point you can try to advance toward setting up a sale.

Classy casual dress will serve your objectives best when having any face-to-face contact with prospective buyers. The right style of dress can create an impression of credibility and may help you to avoid being pushed around. Sometimes it is more profitable to negotiate price with "throw-ins" (e.g., refrigerator, small deck, microwave oven) than with fixed dollars.

The Contract (Offer to Purchase)

It is not possible to cover the entire drafting of a good, thorough offer-to-purchase contract here. It is possible for a small builder to become quite competent in this task with some education, practice, and experience. Most likely a broker or an attorney will draft it. I will, however, cover some concepts that you should be aware of. These are features of the contract that are likely to be a problem and often are not properly geared to the spec home situation no matter who drafts the offer. More often than not, the offer will be executed before the home is 100 percent finished, so you may need an offer that also contains something of a construction contract that covers the remaining work to be done.

The Kickout Clause

You could draft an offer that is contingent upon the sale of the buyer's present home if you use a "kickout clause." This clause allows marketing of your product to continue. When you receive a secondary offer containing references to the first contingency offer, of course, you will notify the first buyers. They will have 48 or 72 hours to either proceed with the purchase or back out and have their earnest money refunded.

Financing Contingencies

Almost all offers require financing contingencies. These must be very specific about type of loan, rate of interest, loan fees, and so on. Allow a fairly tight time schedule for the buyers to obtain a loan commitment. The financing contingency is, in effect, a free option on your home—if the loan is turned down, the extra delay before a closing is reached with another buyer will cost you hundreds of dollars. Specify that you will receive a copy of their loan commitment by the expiration date of the financing contingency; otherwise you then have the option of voiding their contract.

There are three times at which buyers can be required to pay earnest money deposits: with the offer; at the time of acceptance of the offer; and upon approval of financing. Sometimes $100 or even less is submitted with the offer. Instruct brokers that you want several thousand dollars more after your acceptance, and perhaps more upon financing approval, so that you have a total of about 4 to 5 percent of the sale price held in trust right after financing approval. You need this protection. Buyers could default – they may argue and separate, lose their jobs or their life, or just change their minds. Remember that a broker is usually allowed to keep one half of the earnest monies as compensation for finding a buyer, in case the buyer defaults.

Case Study:
The Value of Earnest Money

A buyer's attorney allowed me to keep $5,000 in earnest money on one sale in which no broker was involved. His client had clearly defaulted. She had become nervous about the purchase and about the relationship with the man she lived with. She tried to delay the closing but we held to the closing date and were ready with her color choice in carpet, available for installation before the closing date. She backed out just before carpet installation. The $5,000 was just about the amount we needed to cover the time delay cost to arrive at a later sale at a slightly higher price, and pay for the broker involved.

Property Taxes

Property tax proration is an area that can be problematic. Usually the home you are building either is not assessed or is partially assessed for property tax purposes for the year of sale. You will probably have a tax assessment notice for year of sale in hand by the time of offer. If not, request one. Have your offers specify that proration of taxes at the closing shall be based on this year's tax assessment and last year's tax rate – two known quantities. This will avoid an escrow account for a presently unknown amount and will save you a little money overall.

The Specifications

The builder's construction specifications should be part of the offer. Have these ready when sales efforts begin. The specifications cover the construction that has been completed and describe remaining work. Here you can describe what appliances and other items are included and what items (e.g., driveway pavement) are not included. Variations in the final product made to satisfy the buyers can be described here or in the offer itself. Buyers should sign your copy of the specifications. The lender's appraiser for the buyer will find the specs very helpful.

Costs for Additions and Upgrades

Often buyers request extra features: an increase in the carpeting allowance, extra moldings, and so on. The costs of these features should be collected from the buyers after loan approval and before installation. This money is in addition to the normal earnest monies. You need this protection in case of buyer default or loan disapproval. Usually this extra work will not add value to the home for other buyers.

Undetermined Costs

Avoid the use of escrow accounts to settle costs that cannot be determined at closing. Try to set a price on everything up front. The undetermined cost might be for work that can't be completed because of bad weather or shortages, or municipal assessments for street construction or property taxes. Settling everything at closing frees up your working capital and avoids disputes later.

Builder's Warranty

The offer-contract should cover the builder's warranty in detail, as well as the carpeting selection. I have used this wording: "Builder's warranty shall be until one year after date of closing. Manufacturer's warranties shall pass to buyers. The XYZ home warranty program booklet, "Approved Construction Standards—19ΔΔ", shall apply to all tolerances of workmanship and materials in regard to builder's warranty. A copy of this booklet shall be given to buyers at closing. Buyers understand that this property is not in the XYZ home warranty program."

By using a well-known guideline booklet, you will set specific limits as to what your responsibilities are. Chapter 10 provides more detail on these warranty programs. As for the carpeting, specify that the buyer's choice come from stock that is readily available. You want to avoid waiting for an odd color that the mill can't produce on a regular basis.

Brokers' Addenda

Brokerage firms often have a separate addendum form printed up for their own use or any brokerage board member's use. This addendum is to be attached to the standard state-approved real estate offer form. It can cover the financing contingency in greater detail, or local problems such as radon gas; private sewerage systems; the possibility of large tax or assessment increases resulting from municipal sewer or water problems; compliance with existing building codes; asbestos and lead paints; and so forth. If you or your attorney are drafting your offer, get one of these addendum forms so that you have everything covered in your offer.

The Costs of Sale and Delays

Try to determine all the costs of sale so that you can include this overall cost in the markup on your costs of land, construction, and financing. Marketing costs include your costs related to market research (some of this cost could be charged to design cost) and advertising, if you don't list with a broker right away. Be sure to cover the cost of brochures and signs as well as newspaper advertising. Next, cover the cost of your time spent selling without a broker, or the cost of brokerage services. The total cost of all this can range from a low of 3 percent to a high of 7 percent. A range of 4 to 6 percent is about average, and 4 to 4-1/2 percent is a goal to strive for. A study of well-managed large firms reveals that marketing costs as low as 3.2 percent are possible.

Builders of luxury homes encounter a much thinner market—with a much lower number of annual sales—which requires a higher percentage of marketing expense. Also, the wealthy or powerful buyer can be a real tough negotiator. It is not unusual to encounter at least some degree of bickering over small items in the luxury-home market.

The cost of delays in sale closing is often not given adequate consideration by small builders. Normally, the carrying costs of interest on the funds utilized in the project, tax proration, utility and insurance costs, security protection, and so on can easily be about 1 percent of the sale price per month. This may amount to over $400 per week for a modest move-up home. If delay in a sale slows down your progress in starting or continuing the construction of your next spec home, you have an even greater cost to consider—$1,000 per week or more of lost income. That's why it is so important to have a closing as soon as possible after the completion of construction. You could even consider offering an early-closing credit of a certain dollar amount per day, paid back at closing, to a buyer who wants to close at a date later than necessary.

Summary

Marketing encompasses a wider variety of activities, and is more important, than the average small builder realizes. This chapter includes a great deal of information that you may not have been aware of even if you have been in the business for a while.

Chapter 10 focuses on the events that occur once the sale has been accomplished—financial closing details, builder warranties, and callbacks.

Key Points
- Newspaper advertising can begin as soon as the sheetrock is being installed.
- Don't run an ad for more than two or three weeks without rewriting it or it will become stale.
- A brochure might include reduced-size artist renderings and floor plans, along with a list of features and specifications to satisfy prospects' or brokers' questions.
- The best advertisement is the house itself. Use open houses and clear signage to bring prospects to the home.
- Set three prices for the home: the asking price; the price you will be satisfied with if negotiation is necessary; and a rock-bottom price.
- Buyers may try to obtain a lower price indirectly, by offering to pay the asking price after a number of upgrades and options are added. Be aware of the costs of popular options and upgrades.
- Try to delay the showing of the home until after the drywall has been installed and painted.
- Brokers are the source of 50–75 percent of buyers for the small builder.

- Most experienced brokers tend to concentrate on listing instead of selling if the listing commission is higher.
- Brokers' fees are negotiable, and some brokers have a special rate for builders. A small firm, or the owner of any brokerage firm, is more likely to reduce their commission than a large firm would be. Total commissions of 3 percent to 4.5 percent are possible.
- The offer to purchase will often be executed before the home is 100 percent finished, so you may need an offer that also contains a contract covering the remaining work to be done.
- The cost of delays in sale closings — interest, tax proration, utilities, insurance, etc. — needs to be considered in scheduling the closing as soon as possible after the completion of construction.

Chapter 10
After the Sale: Financial Issues of the Closing, Warranties & Callbacks

Now that you've sold your spec home, you'll want to be sure that the remainder of the process goes smoothly and painlessly. Don't rely entirely on the professionals involved during the sale and prior to the closing to monitor the details as thoroughly as necessary. You may soon have enough experience to realize what is missing and the time needed to get inspections and documents ready.

The Details

Certain items will be needed from the local municipality or state, such as a paid tax bill or certificate, special assessment letter, special code compliance inspection and report, water well test and report, etc. Initiate action on these bureaucratic items yourself to ensure timely deliveries to the title company and buyer's lender. You may also save a few dollars in the process.

See that the lender's appraiser is scheduled for a visit to the home. Try to be there when he or she arrives. You can point out features that the appraiser may have missed, and provide a list of comparable sales in the area that substantiate the value of your product. Most appraisers will appreciate the help, especially if this part of town is a bit unfamiliar.

You may receive some unreasonable requests from the buyer's lender, such as a request for your cost breakdown sheet. This is an item that the lender would need from a builder who is applying for a construction loan. They have no right to insist on this private information from a spec builder. The names of your suppliers and subcontractors will be on the lien waivers that you furnish to the title company. The actual cost and your gross profit are not the lender's business.

Settling Financial Issues at the Closing

"Take the money and run." — Woody Allen

Pay all your bills; get waivers of lien from all the subs and suppliers, and get these to the title insurance company. Be thorough—there are many waivers involved. If you have built this home without a construction loan, the title company, the buyer's attorney, or the lender's attorney may be concerned that a lending institution or title company was not overseeing the payment of bills as construction proceeded. It may help to have receipts or canceled checks on hand in case any lien waivers are challenged. Laws and practices on this vary greatly from state to state.

Most offer-contracts specify that settlement be in cash or certified/cashier's check at closing. This is an important and serious rule that should not be waived at any time. There could be insufficient funds behind a business check. In addition, a business check, or even a non-certified savings-and-loan check, does not begin to earn you interest until it clears the banks. Therefore, you lose one to five days' investment return, not to mention a bit of anxiety over the validity of the check. Also, should you want to conclude the purchase of a building site immediately after the spec home closing, you would not be able to do it with your sale proceeds.

Notify the appropriate parties that you will not close unless you are provided with a cashier's or other certified check that is good as gold at the moment of closing, as per your contract. Your request, several days before closing, should probably be made by registered mail, return receipt. I called ahead to one savings bank and they still tried to give me a less-than-specified type of check. Be aware that some banks may not take you seriously simply because you are a builder rather than a broker or attorney.

Figure 10.1 is an example of a statement of changes and allowance credits after the sale of a home.

The following sections address some other specific financial issues that need to be addressed in most cases.

Carpeting Allowances

The buyer's selection of carpeting can often create several problems. The carpet allowance is a set dollar amount that includes carpet, pad, installation, sales tax, and shipping. If you have adequate time before closing, you can furnish a high-quality carpet direct from the mill for a good price. If time is short, you can specify that the carpet selection be made from a readily available local source. Often carpet salespeople will state that a particular carpet is "in stock" — but the chosen color may have to be set up for a later mill run, delaying your closing by weeks. Advise your buyers to be sure to see the actual carpet roll their material will be cut from to ensure expeditious installation.

Encourage the buyer to select from the most popular colors. Beige is popular, and some shades are particularly attractive. Choosing popular colors allows earlier installation and makes the home look good. Also, you can consider ordering a popular carpet before financing approval. If the loan should be rejected after the carpet is ordered, the carpet will sell easily to the carpet dealer's other customers. If the carpet is installed before the loan rejection, it will not hinder the marketability of the home.

Stipulate that buyers pay the excess cost over allowance directly to the carpet dealer as a non-refundable deposit. Also, insist that buyers pay for any other construction changes before the closing. Your offer-contract should specify carpet allowance, non-refundable payments, and selection/availability

ABC Homes, Inc.

P.O. Box 100, Anywhere, USA 12345

June 26, 19--

To: Mr. and Mrs. John Smith

PRESENT STATUS OF ACCOUNTS: ALLOWANCES AND CHANGES AGAINST $120,000.00
PURCHASE PRICE

	Credits	Debits
Carpet allowance	$1,900.00	
Other allowance	5,000.00	
Refrigerator		947.00
Automatic washer		441.00
Dryer		372.00
Appliance delivery		39.00
Appliance installation labor		30.00
Appliance sales tax (incl. on delivery)		89.95
Flexible gas line and bushing for dryer, incl. tax		7.90
Air conditioning per contract		1750.00
"Aprilaire" per contract		300.00
Laundry cabinets per contract		300.00
Laundry cabinets, 24" high instead of 30"	9.00	
Buyer's purchase of front door paint	7.34	
Total	$6,916.34	$4,276.85

Credit still available: $6,916.34 − 4,276.85 = $2,639.49

Per conversation between Mr. Smith and Builder on June 25, seller (Builder) will come to the closing with a check payable to XYZ Carpeting, Inc. (for carpeting) and Mr. Smith in the amount of $2,639.49.

Figure 10.1 Example of Statement Charges and Allowance Credits After the Sale of a Home

limitations. Most mortgages today are resold on government-sponsored markets that require all rooms, even closets, to have completed finish floor coverings. Often the appraiser will return the day before the closing to check on completion of carpeting and vinyl and hardwood floors.

Title Insurance Savings

Title insurance rates are presented to small builders and to the general public as though they are "set in stone." They have a rate chart/brochure that appears to be set by some distant home office or by the state. The rates probably are, in fact, set by the state, but those rates might be maximum charges. In one state, the deputy commissioner of insurance helped to remove a rule that required title insurance companies to publicly disclose their lowest discounted rates for the insurance commission files. Sometimes there are other charges in addition to the insurance premium, such as application fees, amended report fees, and title examination costs. Over 20 years ago, Senator William Proxmire surveyed a total of 41 title insurance companies. Their net damage claims amounted to only 2.5 percent of their gross income—making this a very profitable industry. A lot more money is paid out in commissions than in claims.

There are several well-known ways for builders to lower title insurance costs.

Requesting Nonissuance of Policy

When you buy the site you can request that the title company not issue the policy, but ask them to hold the file open. Then, when you sell the home, you need to pay only the difference between the premium on the home sale and the lot premium already paid by the lot seller. To this they normally add a flat charge of $40 to $60 for an amended report.

Paying a Special Builder's or Subdivider's Rate

In some states, title insurance companies have a builder's rate, which can be only 60 percent of the standard rate. Or to a subdivider they may offer a master policy for the large tract of land with increases in coverage for each created lot at $2 per extra thousand dollars coverage. However, the small builder usually does not realize that he can also obtain this subdivider rate.

Researching Arrangements with Other Insurance Companies

I started my own search for lower rates after I saw an article in a business paper about the sale of a large, local high-rise office building. Title insurance was furnished at 37 cents per thousand dollars of coverage. After many phone calls, I found a local official of a nationwide title company that agreed to furnish my title insurance at $2 per thousand for the increase in coverage plus the amended report fee. This type of arrangement can save several hundred dollars on each home. In fact, it cut my title insurance costs in half.

Settling Costs Early

Negotiate and verbally settle your title insurance costs before placing your product on the market. Describe the company and your rate arrangement in your brokerage listing contract. Otherwise, you may find your broker ordering out the coverage at the standard rate—maybe from a company with which the brokerage firm has a tie-in or part ownership.

Real Estate Tax Prorations

As explained in Chapter 9, you can avoid uncertainties, possible escrow, and the expenditure of some money by specifying in the sales contract that taxes be prorated on the basis of this year's assessment and last year's (or the latest) rate. Follow up on this point and the simple mathematics involved with those responsible for calculating the closing figures. It is an area in which I have always had to be cautious.

Escrowed Proceeds of Sale

There may be an occasion on which you are unable to avoid an escrow at the closing for taxes or some work included in the sale price that cannot be completed because of weather or shortages. The broker, an attorney, or possibly a title company can act as escrow agent. The document covering the escrow, release of funds, lack of performance, and exact details of work to be done should be carefully drafted. Consider that the new owners may become troublesome, for a variety of personal reasons, after occupying the new home for several months. They may decide to use their power in the escrow to force you to make improvements in the property that are beyond the contract and specifications.

Here is one builder's idea for lowering the number of frivolous phone calls and warranty callbacks from the buyer: an escrow account containing, say, $200 of the builder's own funds is established at the time of closing. Buyers are not told of the "bonus" until closing. The amount of the escrow is included in the purchase price. If the buyers request callback service during the one-year warranty period, the service is billed against the escrow. Whatever escrow funds are unused at the end of one year go to the buyers. One builder reported that 75 percent of his customers qualified to have this entire escrow amount returned to them. In Britain, consumers have to submit a deposit when filing a written complaint to the Builder's Council. If there is substance to the complaint, the deposit is returned.

Warranties and Liabilities

Insurance company-backed new-home warranty programs have been widely promoted as protection that a new home buyer must have. Some home buyers, however, are learning that this protection is not what it seems. These programs were designed for builders by builders; about half of all new homes are covered by them. For the builder, it can be a marketing tool.

When one of the warranty company programs reached my area in the mid-1970s, one of the first to sign on was the worst builder in town. Today, one hears of many instances where builders are not screened before being admitted to these programs, and of inspections never being made during construction. The advertising for these warranty programs has been called misleading by one state regulator. It has been charged that these warranty companies will settle only large claims when the consumer decides to hire an attorney.

There is proposed legislation forbidding the federal government from insuring mortgages on homes covered under these programs. With a reputation like that, don't spend money on warranty company programs unless they are absolutely necessary to selling your product. Your own basic one- or two-year builder's warranty, backed by your reputation and evidence of quality work, is all you should need.

As discussed in Chapter 9, I insert into my sales contracts the reference to a warranty program's "construction standards" book as the guideline about what constitutes a real defect in the home and exactly what is required of the builder to correct it. These standards are a bit easy on the builder, but they are easily accepted by the public and will eliminate some of the more frivolous callbacks. On the other hand, I often make a repair that is not required by the book, for both ethical and public relations reasons. Here is where your judgment and conscience are needed.

The National Association of Home Builders has published a book called *The Builder's Guide to Contracts and Liability*. They have a bookstore in Washington, D.C. and will send a catalog upon request.

Building Materials

Watch out for building materials that are not fully tested. Stay with well-proven products and construction methods. Our court system today can extend your warranty period almost to infinity. You could be liable along with the manufacturer for damages that occur long after the warranty period expires. Three situations come to mind.

Case Study:
Roof Sheathing Product Failures

In 1988, a New Jersey builder received a number of complaints of leaky roofs at a three-year-old condo development. Around the same time, the builder heard about isolated failures, in another area, of FRT roof sheathing used to control the spread of fire in attached housing. The builder took a look at his project and discovered severe FRT-ply degradation throughout the condo development. Replacement costs were estimated at $800,000, or about $1,800 per unit (*Builder,* May 1991).

Case Study:
A Case of Poor Plumbing

Between 1982 and 1985, a builder in Houston used polybutylene plumbing systems in 450 single-family homes. After getting complaints from his plumbers and observing that the fittings were breaking, he went back to using copper piping. In 1989, however, nearly one-fifth of the homes with the polybutylene plumbing experienced plumbing failures. The builder replaced the plumbing in all 450 homes with copper. The process took a year and cost the builder $2 million. Eventually he regained his money in a settlement (*Builder,* May 1991).

Case Study:
Proper Communication of Certain Dangers May Avoid Problems Later

The buyer of a home that I built removed the fixed shower head in the bath and installed a new one on a long flexible hose, without checking with us. Every morning he washed his hair with the sprayer while standing in the tub. Soon the high-pressure spray from his shower head pounded directly at the sheetrock wall above the ceramic tile for long enough to ruin both the sheetrock and the tile wall. The owner expected my company to rebuild his bathroom walls, including tile work, and as a result a long period of lawyer negotiations ensued. All of this could have been avoided by calling out, in writing, the danger of using portable shower heads.

Some damage can be dealt with easily. For example, you may encounter small crack problems in a plastic laminate countertop after occupancy or before. Sometimes the damage is done by the buyers who will not admit to it. Formerly, it was necessary to replace the whole countertop, but now there is a nationwide franchised service that can do flawless, guaranteed repairs for a fraction of the replacement cost.

Callbacks

A survey of builders showed that 83 percent of all warranty callbacks are for minor problems, 16 percent are more serious, and only 1 percent are structural (*Builder,* May 1991, p. 181). The average number of callbacks for each home was a little over three in the first year, and the total average callback cost for each home was about $300. That might be another figure for your cost breakdown sheet.

Attorney Problems and Arbitration

"It is impossible to tell where what is legal ends and where justice begins."
—Anonymous.

While everyone needs an attorney sooner or later, I try to avoid hiring one unless it is absolutely necessary. For those who aren't experienced with attorneys, here are some generalities based on my personal experience. First, the attorney will usually request a sum of money up front (a retainer), which is typically nonrefundable; he or she may or may not provide a detailed account of how the money is used. Furthermore, your own attorney may question you in such a way that challenges your position. The plaintiff's attorney may even use an aggressive approach that may seem intimidating, confusing, or insulting.

Another thing to keep in mind is that it is not necessarily in the attorneys' best interest to settle the case quickly. In the end, you may find that the agreement reached by the attorneys is one that you and the plaintiff could have reached on your own, like splitting the dollar difference. Also, as one problem is solved, the seeds for one or two more problems are sometimes planted. Because of this, attorneys' fees can reach great heights—money that might be saved if the opposing parties could reach agreement before getting attorneys involved.

One attorney, whom I consulted when I was a contract builder, recommended that I use the standard contract of the American Institute of Architects. While this is a widely used document, particularly for larger commercial projects, this contract form is written to protect the architect first, the owner second, and the contractor last. It seems almost inconceivable that an attorney would recommend a document for his builder-client that puts his interests in last place, behind the architect and owner.

I have had other unpleasant experiences with attorneys who delayed closings while they tried to impress their clients by trying to find flaws in an otherwise perfectly handled closing. In one instance where I sold land indirectly to a lawyer, the lawyer closed on the sale in my attorney's office without having most of the money. My attorney allowed this as a professional courtesy. When the check came through a week later, it was only a personal check, which took some work and travel to cash. I received no acknowledgement of this inconvenience from either the attorney or the buyer. I'm sure you've heard even worse stories.

If you receive a threatening letter of complaint from a buyer's attorney, don't react too quickly. After doing your homework, send a letter in reply, calling out the points that back your position. As I have already mentioned, many problems may be resolved without the involvement of attorneys. Furthermore, if you have protected yourself with a good sales contract, there is little likelihood of problems requiring lawsuits.

You might use an arbitration clause that may keep a buyer from hiring a lawyer to go on a "fishing trip." I used this clause in all our building-for-client contracts, but it might also be worth considering for spec building sales.

> *Disputes: Should any dispute arise between the owner and the builder as parties to this contract, such dispute shall be settled through arbitration by either the American Arbitration Association or the National Academy of Conciliators. The decision of the Arbitrators shall be final and binding. Should either party hire a lawyer before exhausting the arbitration process, that party agrees to pay for the attorney costs of the other party.*

Of course, attorneys don't like this clause but none have ever been effective in getting it removed from our contracts.

When hiring an attorney to represent you or do any other work, be sure to check him or her out thoroughly and verify his or her real estate experience. Legal fees need to be watched, as they can vary widely. Ascertain all costs up front. My suggestion is to contact the HALT (Help Stop American Legal Tyranny) organization in Washington, D.C. They are a great watchdog organization. One of their mottos is, "America has 800,000 lawyers and they all like to eat lunch." For low cost or a donation they can provide you with booklets on how to hire an attorney and endless other matters you should be aware of. Before closing the subject, let me say that there are certainly many good and decent attorneys; I have had one for the past 13 years.

Customer Relations

You want your buyers to be pleased with your product. After the closing, provide them with a list of mechanical contractors and tell them that they may call them directly if a real emergency arises during the warranty period when you are not available. Recommend a few reputable contractors that they may need for future landscaping, pavements, or other improvement work. You will, of course, be furnishing them with a copy of the "Construction Standards" booklet. Also, provide a quart or gallon of interior wall paint to use in touch-ups after they move in furniture.

If you do not hear from the homeowners for many months, stop in or call to see how everything is during the warranty period. Inform them about your present spec projects—they might know of a prospective buyer.

Summary

Obviously, your work is not over just because the sale is complete. There are a lot of details still to work out—and not every one may have been mentioned in this chapter. The number and complexity of details to be dealt with after the sale will vary in each situation, and in each location. As you become more experienced and established in your business, the process will be more likely to run smoothly and efficiently.

Chapter 11 covers proper handling of paperwork and planning—both of which are overlooked by many small builders despite the fact that they are essential in maintaining any size business.

Key Points
- Try to be present when the lender's appraiser visits the home.
- Pay all your bills and have receipts on hand in case any lien waivers are challenged at the time of the closing.
- Ensure that settlement will be in cash or certified/cashier's check.
- Encourage the buyer to choose from the most popular carpet colors, and stipulate that the buyer pay the excess cost over allowance directly to the carpet dealer.
- Investigate ways to lower title insurance costs: request nonissuance of policy, pay a special builder's rate, research arrangements with other insurance companies, and settle title costs early.
- Don't spend money on warranty company programs unless they are absolutely necessary to selling your product. Your own builder's warranty is all you should need.
- Beware of building materials that are not fully tested.
- Try not to hire an attorney unless it is absolutely necessary. In the end, you may find that the agreement reached by attorneys is one that you and the opposing party could have reached on your own.
- During the warranty period, stop in or call buyers of your spec home to see how everything is and to inform them of your current projects.

Chapter 11
Planning for Profit & Continuity

Good organization is one essential key to the success of many projects. Another is proper planning, both short and long term. Continuing your education, anticipating market changes, and investing for retirement are also part of the planning process. Each of these concerns is addressed in this final chapter.

Organizing Yourself and Your Paperwork

Throughout the course of each project, you should keep good records of everything—from market research to subcontractor information to building material warranties. Records from one project will invariably be useful to you in subsequent projects. The financial aspects of proper organization include bookkeeping and income tax issues.

Maintaining Files

The many notes, estimates, material lists, etc., that you accumulate for each project should be kept in a good filing system throughout the design, construction, and closing process. For example, I use 13 separate files for each home. The file folders are color coded, as are the plastic racks they are placed in. The use of three colors—blue, red, and black—allow for the construction of up to three homes at a time. Each home's set of files is kept in a separate rack. The names of the files that I use are as follows:

- Real Estate and Insurance
- Market Research, Design, Engineering, and Cost Breakdown
- Building Permit
- Survey, Utilities, Site Work, and Excavation
- Rough Trades, plus Concrete and Masonry
- Lumber, Windows and Exterior Doors
- Mechanical Trades
- Cabinets, Counters, and Interior Millwork
- Finish Trades
- Floor Covering: Vinyl, Ceramic, Hardwood, Carpet
- Appliances, Finish Hardware, Mirrors, and Light Fixtures

- Paid Bills and Waivers
- Sale of Home

On the outside of the Paid Bills and Waivers file, I list payments, dates of payments, check numbers, and whether or not the waiver is in the file.

In the files for various trades and materials, you might include a recap sheet where all bids for each trade or set of materials are listed on a separate sheet. This will make it easier to quickly compare bid prices.

Any of these files can easily travel to your job site, subs, or suppliers in your attache case. This system has worked well for me, but there are other good systems. You may come to develop your own methods over the course of building a number of homes.

The computer can be a great help here also. You may need to use a scanner to get all material and subcontractor billings onto a computer disk. Otherwise, some seemingly insignificant detail may not be available when you need it later. A computerized file system may also allow you to cross-reference your files in more ways than you could with a traditional paper file.

Bookkeeping

Bookkeeping is really comprised of two elements: cost accounting and profit/loss accounting.

Cost accounting should be an ongoing effort to remain aware of all the individual costs that go into a home. Keep your cost breakdown sheet up to date about twice a month in the final cost column—in pencil, not pen. Note costs that might be forgotten, along with color choices and model numbers needed for reference when building future homes, in your job notebook, which should accompany you every day. Your checkbook should be the type with enough space on the stub for detailed notes on items paid for. Keep records of paid bills in your filing system. Keep track of receipts for the few small items you pay for with cash.

With this type of organization, you can easily enter items into a bookkeeping ledger system that states your profit/loss annual income; you can then easily transfer the figures to Schedule C of your income tax return. For a little extra money, you might consider the purchase of a bookkeeping system with checks combined in an ongoing journal. I use a small cash ledger book to record the receipt of sale proceeds as well as other income such as rebates and insurance refunds.

Other checklists, material lists, specifications, and so on appear throughout this book. There is one other accounting form that can be helpful in getting a long-term view of how your business is doing. If you are building the same home design over and over, lay out a very wide cost breakdown sheet so that you can observe the changes in the final cost of each item from home to home (from left to right on the vertical columns that cover each home). In this way, you can get a perspective on costs that are rising too fast, staying the same, or even dropping, and then concentrate your efforts where improvements can be made.

Watch over large costs with much more intensity than small costs. Don't get bogged down in the penny ante areas. If you work too hard at saving small change, you may be too busy to be effective at saving big money on larger purchases.

Dealing with Income Taxes

Our income tax system is not always kind to small business people. Self-employment tax can be larger than either the federal or state income tax for a spec builder doing just two homes per year. The percentage of total tax you pay on the last dollar that you earn in December can be higher than the total percentage on the last dollar of income for someone whose income is ten times greater than yours.

One year I ran all the numbers for after-tax income after building one spec home per year, compared to two homes, then compared to three homes. The extra after-tax income on the second home was about 47 percent of the income from the first home; and the increased, after-tax income on the third home was 50 percent of the first home. The jump from 47 percent to 50 percent was mostly a result of income beyond the self-employment tax limit. It can be a bit discouraging to know that three income taxes (federal, state, and self-employment) can add up to a marginal rate of almost 50 percent on the second or third home you build.

Take whatever business deductions the law allows, but be careful about office-in-the-home deductions. Be sure of where you stand on that point. Review the IRS guide booklet that covers the use of a home office. You can contribute to a tax-deferred retirement account, but these funds will then not be available as business capital. The tax deduction, however, is great. You will have to decide how much money, if any, you should tie up in your retirement account each year, based on future capital needs as well as retirement requirements.

The choice of the legal form of your business organization for tax, business liability, and insurance cost considerations is a very complex consideration. You will need to do a bit of reading, then meet with an attorney, an accountant, and an insurance consultant with your tax returns and business plan in hand.

The Spec Builder's Lifestyle

Some of the advantages to a career in spec building were discussed in Chapter 1. One advantage to being a spec builder is that this business offers many options in lifestyle. You can determine your own schedule. You can take a vacation after the completion of each home if you want to. As you near retirement, you may want to work only during certain times of the year, and spend the warmer months living in a cooler climate or the cooler months living in a warmer climate.

It is to your business advantage to live in a new home that is similar to or the same as the spec home(s) you are producing. This will allow you to have a new home every three to five years. Or you could build a vacation home for your own use for several years, then sell out at a profit. The homes that you occupy will bring a larger profit than your spec homes. There is no need to offer a low price—you have the use of the property while awaiting a good offer. The property has more value because you have added final touches to pavements, landscaping, etc., and a furnished home shows well. Your home could rise in value faster than the general market as a result of the increased popularity of your location. The sale of your own residence can offer tax savings through use of capital gains versus earned income and through tax deferrals and forgiveness. Many builders move from one new home to another quite often to build up their capital. Build and profitably sell five homes this way and the last one is, essentially, free. One man I know became a wealthy owner of many apartment buildings. He graduated from the school of dentistry but immediately began building a home for himself, which he sold quickly. He lived in 17 homes in this way, which built up his capital. This type of disruptive living, however, is not necessary unless you wish to make money your only priority.

This business offers you the choice of doing work that you enjoy and avoiding work that you do not enjoy. For example, if you enjoy architectural design, do all of it. If you don't like dealing with subcontractors or buyers, hire someone else to do it.

It is possible to fully retire after only five or ten years in this business. You will need to work hard and expertly, and have the home building cycle in your favor. If you do retire early, you can always go back to work temporarily by building one home every year or even every other year. The subject of retirement planning is discussed further a bit later in this chapter.

Beware of becoming overconfident after some success. As Winston Churchill said, "Success is never final." This business has swollen many egos to dangerous proportions. Building requires discipline. Some favorable personality traits in a spec builder include self-denial, self-discipline, control of greed and fear, goal orientation, being realistic, self-criticizing, and dedication to making improvements.

Developing a Long-term Perspective

Building one spec home is real estate development on the smallest scale—the essence of capitalism. Each piece of real estate—each spec home—is a separate business. You have the ability to bounce back from a poor showing on each project. No home project will ever proceed exactly as you had planned. If you are fairly new to this field, get some names of builders that subs and suppliers feel are well organized and successful. Study their operations as much as possible.

As you expand your annual production, remember to multiply yourself. Hire out design work, expediting, cleanup work, sales, or other tasks. Don't run yourself into the ground by trying to do too much. Your business will not benefit.

An important step in long-term planning is determining how many homes you can build per year and, with that in mind, developing a five-year business plan.

How Many Homes Per Year?

Many working capital and lending policies restrict the number of spec homes that small builders can produce in a year. If you can finance only one home at a time, your production will be limited to two or three homes per year.

You may have to start in this business as many others have: build a spec-oriented home for your own use and sell it after a few months of occupancy. Then rent an apartment or house to live in while you start the next home.

If you can finance the construction of two homes at a time, annual production will be large enough to fully utilize your time for all managerial tasks. Two homes at one time will require less capital if construction start dates are staggered by about six to eight weeks. With enough funds to build three homes at one time, your managerial hours will make for a long work week. With a volume like that, however, you can easily afford to hire managerial assistance.

Don't be concerned about needing to increase your business volume to survive. Your first goals should be to obtain more profit per home than your competitors, and to produce homes that sell fast.

One strategy that might be useful is to take a spec home to the rough mechanicals stage and into a "lock up" condition. Start marketing the home just before reaching this stage and, if it doesn't sell by that point, start building a second home. In this way, you will be continuing to produce more homes over a period of time, instead of slowing down.

The highest comfortable volume for a small spec-only builder is about ten homes per year. I observed one well-organized small spec builder in the Pacific Northwest who advertised that his production was limited to ten homes per year to ensure high quality and attention to detail. This makes sense for both the builder and the consumer.

A Five-Year Business Plan

Most new entrepreneurs in building construction are not familiar with writing a business plan — a workable plan with reachable goals for the first years of operation. It is a far better idea than flying by the seat of your pants, allowing outside influences to control your destiny. Many of the fast-growing new high-tech industries were started by educated people who spent as much as a year formulating their business plan before operations began.

Your plan will be limited by your expertise, your capital, the business cycle, and the local market. When starting from the bottom, plan on doing one home at a time and saving money like a squirrel saves nuts so you will have the funds to step up production as your experience grows. In the latter half of the first five years, you may have set aside enough funds to be able to build a two- to four-family rental building for investment purposes (building duplexes is discussed later in this chapter). Consider revising your plan annually.

Plan for Good and Bad Times

There will always be good times and bad times in speculative home building. In good times, land and responsive subcontractors are difficult to find. In bad times, sales are not easy. There have been 11 new housing cycles between

1946 and 1993—one new cycle about every four to five years. The change in the price of common stocks in large home building corporations reflects the anticipated national trends in the cycle. Consider where you are in the cycle when writing your five-year plan. What you do wrong often has less of a long-term effect on income than what you fail to do or fail to take advantage of.

Add to Your Company When Necessary

It is quite possible to build a little organization of two to three people soon after starting your business. You will then be able to work at tasks where you are most effective. The maximum production potential can be as high as 14 homes per management person, or 160 to 200 hours per home. A cyclical slowdown can cut back on this quickly, however. You may have to lay off some hired management help and/or cut back on your crew during bad times.

Develop Your Own Business Strategy

Your plan should contain some business strategy and policy. Plan to deal with management errors in land purchasing or design choices by selling out without much profit quickly, if necessary, or by eliminating bad subs or other bad components quickly. It's usually better to take a small beating now than a larger one later, so cut your losses quickly. The best overall policy is to build it good and build it fast. A number of case studies related throughout this book have illustrated these concepts.

Maintain a Commitment to Your Primary Business

Try to avoid the temptation to get involved in sideline ventures such as building on contract, remodeling on contract, or buying homes to rehabilitate. Remodeling requires a different set of subcontractors than new construction, and the profits are quite erratic.

Stay the course on spec building if at all possible, and try to concentrate your work in one general location so that you get to know it really well. A limit of a 25-mile radius from your home is a good policy. Rather than spend money on business image advertising or overly-sophisticated design, put the money into the homes so you can offer value.

Building duplexes—either for investment purposes or as spec projects—and land speculation are two options that some spec builders consider.

Building Duplexes

Building a multi-family dwelling for investment purposes can be a good idea. Building a duplex or two-family town house as a spec project is another idea. Not all communities have zoning that allows this type of housing. If this type of housing is allowed, the buildings are often used as buffers between commercial and single-family areas. Some duplex subdivisions are in fine locations, especially if they are built as condominiums rather than rentals.

The main problem in building a duplex on speculation is that gross profits are usually a bit tight. Duplex buyers are usually focused on lowering the cost of living or investment returns. They are not as emotional about their choice of residence and can be tough negotiators. In addition to a lowered percentage of gross profit, some of your callback problems are doubled: two furnaces, more doors and windows, more plumbing, and so on.

Duplexes should be built for investment, even if it is only for a short holding period. They will return about one percentage point less as an investment compared to a large apartment building but you may be able to attract a higher-caliber tenant who is apt to take good care of your property. Living in a new, well-designed duplex unit is a step up from an apartment, and the building can be almost as attractive as a detached single-family home. You should never have a vacancy and always have a good choice of tenants because of the tremendous market demand for this kind of living unit.

Duplex ownership will tie up some of your working capital, so it is practical only when you have excess spare capital, are approaching retirement, or are retired. A program of building duplexes, holding them for two to six years, and selling them to get your capital out can lead to a rich retirement. The advantages are inflationary appreciation, no time pressure on sales, rent increases, and income tax advantages. Sell a like-new duplex before any repairs are needed and free up your capital. Good duplexes sell as swiftly as single-family homes. A small builder might consider one as a personal residence when starting out.

The designs and floor plans should be as close as possible to single-family features and privacy. Don't build a duplex that is too large or too costly, however. The required rent may be difficult to obtain, and tenant turnover may be high if the rent is as high or higher than monthly payments on a new home.

Turning your duplex into condos and selling the building in two parts should produce a total sale price that is at least 10 percent higher. If you plan to do this at the end of your holding period, begin at least some of the legal work before construction, and design the duplex with this in mind.

Land Speculation

Buying a few sites before they are needed for building homes is fine if they can be purchased at bargain prices or are unique sites. This way you'll have two options: sell the bare site later for a speculator's profit, or build on it for a builder's profit.

Turning a tract of raw land into completed building lots is another matter. Land development is much more risky and complex than home building. The time span from purchase of a tract to the sale of the last lot can take from two to five or more years. I would advise the average spec builder to stay away from this field. You will be competing with experienced full-time operators. If you must try it, do it with an experienced joint-venture partner (but see the caveats about engaging in a joint venture in Chapter 7).

Land development usually requires rezoning and land division approval. Meeting with these officials requires a certain degree of subservience and tact, together with a display of competent thoroughness. Having your attorney in the background at meetings can help. You will have to do work with neighbors and their leaders early on. This process can really pay off. Land that has zoning approval sometimes increases in value by 50 percent immediately.

Retirement Planning

"I started with nothing and I still have most of it." — Milton Berle

The building business can consume all of your energy and almost all of your free time. Like many enterprises, the business can run you rather than allow you to run the business. A workaholic can find all the work he or she desires as a builder. A builder can work almost around the clock, seven days a week. Many of us recognize that this demanding work is not what we might want to do — or be able to do — for very many years. Try to control your business so it is not detrimental to your health, to your family, or to a balanced life. Working, growing, and saving toward some type of retirement should be part of your business plan.

Rather than retiring completely, you might consider moving into a related business or occupation that is less demanding. Our society rewards manipulative behavior better than productive behavior, so you could ease off by going with the flow and becoming one of the manipulators.

Retirement Investments

"I am a better businessman because I am an investor. I am a better investor because I am a businessman." — Warren Buffet

Many builders ensure a steady retirement income by building a number of residential rental units as a rather permanent investment. By building these rentals yourself, your markup becomes a good part of your equity, and your cash equity requirements are considerably less than those of other investors. Net income is the same as for all cash equity. If you do not enjoy managing property and dealing with tenants, you might hire someone to perform these tasks.

Investing in a portfolio of securities consisting of stocks and bonds will also provide for retirement. Mutual funds offer the safety of diversification and free up your time by including professional management.

Builders who are familiar with real estate investment usually lack familiarity and ease with securities investment. On the other hand, people who know a lot about securities often know little about direct real estate investment. You should try to be well versed in both, and should allocate some of your funds into each type of investment. As you learn more about securities, analysis, and evaluation, you will find that this knowledge will make you a better business manager. Of course, expertise in managing your business can be applied to evaluating securities, especially those of large home building firms.

Investment in rental properties that you construct may pay a better return than securities. After all, by investing in rentals you eliminate almost all the intermediaries that stand between you and the income — no brokers, portfolio management firms, corporate executives, corporate tax collectors, etc.

In order to avail yourself of the benefits of compound interest, you should begin setting aside funds for retirement as early as possible. This might be easier said than done. The spec builder needs capital — lots of it. If you invest capital as part of your equity in new rental property with a large mortgage, it is no longer available for use in your spec building business unless you sell the rental. If you invest retirement funds in securities (outside of tax deferred plans), you can borrow funds quickly and easily through your bank or broker.

The law allows 50 percent of the value of one's securities to be lent to the owner, and several of the large discount securities brokerage firms will lend on mutual funds. The broker loan rates are usually close to the bank prime rate.

Being an Educated Builder

Spec home building requires a considerable amount of knowledge in many areas. Throughout your career, it is important to remain educated about current trends and technology in the industry. This includes being involved in appropriate organizations and associations, taking classes and seminars, and reading widely.

The National Association of Home Builders

The National Association of Home Builders is a very good organization, especially as a resource for educational materials from their large bookstore and supplier/subcontractor contacts for the new builder.

I suspect that the brokerage industry may have a little too much influence in some local NAHB chapters in maintaining high commission rates charged to builders. When I wrote a letter to my local chapter about the inflexibility of these rates and suggested what builders, as a group, could do about them, I didn't receive an encouraging reply from the local executive director. He felt this was not an issue and said it had not been raised before. Fortunately, shortly thereafter I met a broker who handled my homes for a lower commission than I had outlined in my letter to the local builder's association.

Nonetheless, the NAHB does an outstanding job with research, education, and looking out for builders' interests in governmental legislation. They are worthy of support.

Continuing Education Programs

Your level of expertise has a greater effect on your income than effort expended or money spent. Continue to read widely, look for classes and seminars, and observe new trends in new home building wherever you travel as well as in your own region.

Several years ago, the National Association of Home Builders began a seminar program called the "Graduate Builder's Institute." These series of two- to three-day courses are available in several states. Attendance twice a year for two years leads to certification. Most of the courses are focused on running a business, along with some technical instruction. Another benefit to attending these courses is the opportunity to meet with fellow students and discuss common problems.

Identification of Market Changes and Design Trends

Active small builders often recognize market change more quickly than large builders and can respond to them faster. Don't confuse a short disruption in the market with a long-term trend. You may be observing just a blip in the pattern. Many people assume existing trends will carry on indefinitely, whether that trend is to higher interest rates, tighter money, smaller family units, whatever. The universe consists of circles and curves. Everything that is perceived as a straight line is probably part of a large curve.

Interest Rate Variations

Interest rate increases can have a very damaging effect on your business, as homes are more difficult to sell and sale prices become soft. By using the interest rate options or futures market, you may be able to hedge your position. Make a profit in options or futures that equals your profit setback on home sales. The lumber futures market offers the same possibility to offset the cost of higher lumber prices.

This is not a game for amateurs. You'll need to get educated first. As discussed in Chapter 7, there are more losers than winners among the participants in this market.

Home Size Variations

We have experienced a long trend to larger and larger homes. Sooner or later — probably sooner — this trend will halt or reverse. Our American economy will probably not be in a global position to allow us such excess consumption. Larger, multi-generational family units require larger homes, but that implies bunching up formerly-separated small family units, as when unemployed, married children return to their parents' home.

A home designed with a first-floor bedroom suite or two master bedrooms makes sense for an aging population and for live-in grandparents or mature single children that return home. In some areas with high housing costs, homes are being built with small efficiency one-bedroom au-pair or in-law apartments. In some cases, the real purpose of such an arrangement may be to rent the unit out to a working single person, which may, in some areas, be a violation of one-family zoning.

You might be tempted to consider building homes using factory-built sections or modules, especially when subs are too busy and costs are rising fast. Lower costs per square foot and much faster construction cycles are touted as great reasons for moving away from stick building. However, total costs are often not as low as forecast, and I've seen construction cranes struggle in the mud to erect a panelized factory-built house that then needs a week of carpentry to complete the shell. Where is the time savings? Factory-built housing probably should be used only in conditions of flat, roomy sites; well-built and well-designed, complete modules; and perfect coordination of construction activity. Even then, the homes should be small, and built within a short distance from the factory.

Being Your Own Consultant

Although business consultants are available for hire by individual builders, the cost is prohibitive for most small operators. However, you can keep a few principles and guidelines in mind so that you can, to a degree, be your own consultant.

The following principles review many of the strategies and methods that have been discussed throughout this book.

If your operation is not going as it should, your first and most significant task is to diagnose the problem. Go through last year's books and see how your gross profit, various overhead categories, and net profit compare with the ratios and margins discussed in Chapter 2.

Low sales volume could easily be a problem if you don't have enough sales to spread over the overhead costs that are fixed. Your annual sales could be three times your net worth if you don't use construction loans, and about six times your net worth if you do use them.

Are you attracting enough traffic to look at your homes, and is it the right kind of traffic? Are you listing your homes through multi-listing services? Do at least 25 percent of the sale prospects come back for a second look?

If you handle your own sales, are you building where people can easily find your homes? Are you spending between 1 percent and 1-1/2 percent on advertising? Do your ads need to be revised?

If browsers do not return, perhaps you are not offering enough value. Thoroughly compare your offering with the competition and consider changes in design or location. Is the cost of construction about 55 percent of the sales price? Can you redesign your product to offer more value and architectural appeal?

Remember, you are not in business to see how many homes you can build. You are in business to make a profit. An established builder should get a 25 to 50 percent return on his or her business investment, which is almost all working capital. Some builders have constructed a great number of homes but ended up with little or nothing. Your final costs should not vary more than 1 percent or 2 percent from your estimates. A building firm that completes 200 homes per year can have a higher dollar profit than a firm that builds 4,000 homes annually.

Don't get involved in too many different home designs. Once you have your annual production up to a profitable and comfortable level, why expand? That could be too risky.

Don't spread yourself too far geographically. Jobs that are over an hour's drive away are too far.

It is easy to develop an ego problem from the quick success that often occurs in this business. Once that happens, you can lose some connection with reality, and your control and caution may be diminished.

Starting in a New Location

The only really good business reason for moving to a new location is that business is bad in your area, with little chance for improvement, and much better where you are headed. Check out the volatility of the number of single-family permits issued over a long period in the proposed new area. You could be heading into an area that is very cyclical—the next bust may be just over the hill.

You will have a very heavy initial workload in a new location: basic market research, finding good subs and suppliers, and all of the other tasks discussed earlier in this book. Consider hiring a superintendent who is well acquainted with local subs. Or hire a good, local, small custom builder as your construction manager for a flat or hourly fee to help with advice about design, subs, and suppliers. Let him expedite your first home or two. After having experienced the problems and strain of relocating myself, this is exactly what I would do.

Surviving as a Spec Builder

Wherever you choose to build homes, you can be proud of being a small builder/developer, despite the lack of respect you may experience from some people in the industry's ancillary professions. Your creations, undertaken at your own risk, provide the population with one of their most desired and basic needs—an attractive, well-built, and economical home that holds its value well. Not many others can create something of lasting value where nothing stood before.

Of course, this business is not for everyone. You need to be mature about finances. You must be able to practice self-denial. You need to be disciplined in your business practice. You must be very careful with money. This is what is needed to survive as a spec builder and to build up your capital so that you can bring your annual sales volume up to a comfortable and profitable level without dependence on construction loans.

It is not difficult to build a cheap, small house. On the other hand, it is also fairly easy to build an expensive, large home that is quite beautiful. There are many builders who are successful, at least for a while, with either of these products. Your challenge is to create the most value in an attractive home that can be sold in a popular price range, year after year.

Key Points
- The notes, estimates, material lists, etc., that you accumulate for each project should be kept in a good filing system.
- Cost accounting should be an ongoing effort to remain aware of all the individual costs that go into a home. Keep your cost breakdown sheet up to date about twice a month—in pencil.
- The highest comfortable volume for a small spec builder without hired staff is about 10 homes per year.
- Write a business plan with reachable goals for the first years of your business.
- Stay educated in your field: read widely, look for classes and seminars, and pay attention to new trends. The NAHB is a good resource for educational materials and contacts.
- Try to control your business so it is not detrimental to your health, to your family, or to a balanced life.
- Start planning for your retirement as early as possible.
- Try to recognize market changes and trends for what they are—don't confuse a short disruption in the market with a long-term trend.
- Building a duplex for investment purposes can be a good idea. Don't build a duplex that is too large or costly.
- Relocation means a heavy initial workload, engaging in all the steps that are discussed earlier in this book—market research, finding good subs and suppliers, and so on.
- Beware of becoming overconfident after some success; be disciplined, realistic, and dedicated to making improvements.

Resources Appendix

Recommended Readings

Architecture and Home Design

Alexander, Christopher, et al. *A Pattern Language.* New York: Oxford, 1977.
A book that resulted from wide-ranging research by six or more academics into timeless building types and details that have appealed to various cultures throughout history. A unique, classic book about patterns and details with universal appeal, from region/neighborhood to windows and closets.

Brangham, Suzanne. *Housewise.* New York: Harper & Row, 1987.
A book about intensive remodeling, but you can learn much about design and color choices from the all-important woman's point of view.

Faulkner, Ray, and Faulkner, Sarah. *Inside Today's Home.* New York: Holt, Rinehart, & Winston, 1968.
A classic college textbook, covering design of rooms, color choices, and other factors affecting the interior design of a home.

Grant, Donald P. *The Small-Scale Master Builder.* P.O. Box 5, San Luis Obispo, CA, 1983.
Spec and investment building ideas for the under-employed architect, written by an architect-professor.

Link, David E. *Residential Designs.* Boston: Cahners, 1974.
Cost/value effective design considerations from house siting to closet design, by the former editor of *Professional Builder*.

McAlester, Lee, and McAlester, Virginia. *A Field Guide to American Houses.* New York: Knopf, 1984.
A comprehensive guide to all historical styles and their unique details. Encourages the reader to know the past and develop a feel for designs that withstand the test of time.

Moore, Charles, Allen, George, and Lyndon, Donlyn. *The Place of Houses.* New York: Holt, Rinehart, & Winston, 1974.
Some thoughts by three leading architects.

Parker, Harry. *Simplified Engineering for Architects and Builders.* New York: Wiley, 1975.

A very technical book; read only those parts that apply to problems encountered with single-family homes. Several chapters help the builder understand some complex structural considerations.

Rasmussen, Steen Eiler. *Experiencing Architecture.* Cambridge, MA: MIT Press, 1959.

The classic book about architectural principles — surfaces, solids, cavities, scale, proportion, rhythm, daylight, and color — written so that even a 14-year-old could understand it.

Simonds, John O. *Landscape Architecture.* New York: McGraw-Hill, 1961.

Timeless principles for the home site and general house design.

Stegman, George K., and Stegman, Harry J. *Architectural Drafting.* Second edition. Chicago, IL: American Technical Society, 1974.

A very good overall textbook on home design and drafting techniques. If this book is not available, similar titles should suffice. The second edition of this book is available as a paperback reprint from Books on Demand, Ann Arbor, Michigan.

Stitt, Fred A. *Systems Drafting.* New York: McGraw-Hill, 1980.

Drafting ideas that save time and improve detail.

Note: The Prairie Avenue Bookstore in Chicago is probably the largest store in the country that deals exclusively in architectural books. They issue a catalog/book list and can probably furnish many of the books listed here as well as some on construction management and techniques for home builders.

Business Management

Baty, Gordon B. *Entrepreneurship: Playing to Win.* Reston, VA: Reston Publishing Co. (a Prentice-Hall company), 1974.

A very good book on general business management.

Fields, Alan, and Fields, Denise. *Your New House.* Boulder, CO: Windsor Peak Press, 1994.

A consumer's guide — good sections on brokers, warranty companies, designers, etc.

Halpin, Michael C. *Profit Planning for Real Estate Development.* Homewood, IL: Dow-Jones Irwin, 1977.

Covers large residential condo and rental projects.

Hawken, Paul. *The Next Economy.* New York: Ballantine, 1983.

Evolving world business changes that contain ideas for the small entrepreneur.

Higson, James D. *The Higson Home Builder's Guide.* Carlsbad, CA: Craftsman Book Co., 1977.

Covers contract luxury home construction in southern California.

"How to be an Operative Home Builder." Transcript of New Ventures School. Washington, DC: Housing Capital Corp., 1979.
From lectures given by many professionals over a one-week intensive course in all areas of builder business management.

Karrass, Chester L. *Give and Take.* New York: Thomas Y. Crowell, 1974.
A book on negotiating by one of the best teachers of this subject, with over 200 tactics and strategies covered in alphabetical articles.

Karrass, Chester L. *The Negotiating Game.* New York: Thomas Y. Crowell, 1970.
A basic beginning text that covers the process of negotiating from start to finish.

Phillippo, Gene. *The Professional Guide to Real Estate Development.* Homewood, IL: Dow-Jones Irwin, 1976.
Contains many principles of use to the small home builder, even though the book is about development of a large rental project.

Smolkin, William R. *A Marketing Strategy for the Seventies for Small-Volume Builders.* Washington, DC: National Association of Home Builders, 1967.
An excellent management guide by an industry consultant.

Note: All builders should subscribe to the following periodicals:
Professional Builder *(1350 E. Touhy Ave., Des Plaines, IL 60018-3358)*
Builder *(One Thomas Circle, Suite 600, Washington, DC 20005)*

Construction Trades and Materials

Anderson, L.O. *Wood Frame House Construction.* U.S. Government Printing Office, 1970 and later.
The classic book on basic wood frame construction.

Emerson, Larry, and Oleksy, Walter. *Builder and Contractor's Guide to New Methods and Materials in Home Construction.* Englewood Cliffs, NJ: Prentice-Hall, 1983.
Provides cost-saving construction techniques for management and building trades.

Hageman, Jack. *Contractor's Guide to the Building Code.* Carlsbad, CA: Craftsman Book Co., 1983.
An excellent guide to interpreting the local building code and avoiding errors not covered by the building inspector's plan checker.

Housing and Urban Development Agency (HUD). *Reducing Home Building Costs with OVE Design and Construction.* Washington, DC: U.S. Government Printing Office, 1980.
Similar to NAHB manual (see next entry), but includes other trades, using the Optimum Value Engineered building system.

National Association of Home Builders. *Manual of Lumber and Plywood Saving Techniques.* Rockville, MD: NAHB Research Foundation, 1971.
A manual filled with money-saving ideas.

Reed, Mortimer P. *Residential Carpentry*. New York: Wiley, 1980.
A well-organized and well-illustrated book covering from start of framing to interior trim.

Contracts and Legal Issues

National Association of Home Builders. *Contracts and Liability for Builders and Remodelers*. Third edition. Washington, DC: NAHB, 1993.
A guide to contracts, disclaimers, and warranties with sample language and checklists.

Real Estate

Benke, William. *All About Land Investment*. New York: McGraw-Hill, 1976.
Written for land investors, but contains many ideas to help in site selection.

Rene, Henry A., Jr. *How to Profitably Buy and Sell Land*. New York: Wiley, 1977.
A book for land speculators and subdividers, but very educational for the small builder.

Ring, Alfred A. *The Valuation of Real Estate*. Engelwood Cliffs, NJ: Prentice-Hall, 1963 and later.
The classic text on real estate values.

Unger, M. A. *Real Estate: Principles and Practices*. Chicago: Southwestern Publishing, 1964.
A great basic textbook; an introduction to the field of real estate.

Various authors. *Investing in Raw Land*. Boston: Warren, Gorham, and Lamont, 1980 and later.
A professional guide, with forms, from a real estate specialty publisher. Each article or chapter is written (from seminar speeches, in some cases) by a different academic or professional.

Reference Books

DelPico, Wayne J. *Plan Reading and Material Takeoff*. Kingston, MA: R.S. Means Co., 1994.
A guide to reading and interpreting building plans, and performing quantity takeoffs to professional standards, for residential and light commercial construction.

Fleming, John, Honour, Hugh, and Pevsner, Nikolaus.
The Penguin Architectural Dictionary. Baltimore, MD: Penguin, 1966.
This book is probably not available now, but any dictionary of architectural terms as well as a building trades dictionary are "must have" reference books. See entry for *Means Illustrated Construction Dictionary* on the next page.

Frisby, Thomas N. *How to Survive and Prosper in Construction*. Kingston, MA: R.S. Means Co., 1990.
Outlines a checklist system for organizing, managing, and marketing a construction firm successfully.

Means Estimating Handbook. Kingston, MA: R.S. Means Co., 1990.
A handbook for evaluating plans and specifications to obtain reliable quantities for pricing.

Means Forms for Contractors. Kingston, MA: R.S. Means Co., 1990.
Includes a variety of forms for each phase of the project, from bidding to punch list. Each blank form is accompanied by a filled-in example.

Means Forms for Building Construction Professionals. Kingston, MA: R.S. Means Co., 1990.
A three-ring binder containing forms for all primary construction activities that can be customized with your company name and reproduced on a photocopier.

Means Illustrated Construction Dictionary. Kingston, MA: R.S. Means Co., 1991.
A complete construction dictionary with over 17,000 construction terms, words, phrases, acronyms, and abbreviations, and hundreds of illustrations.

Heuer, Charles R. *Means Legal Reference for Design and Construction*. Kingston, MA: R.S. Means Co., 1989.
Provides answers to common legal questions and points out practical implications of larger issues that you may encounter in construction.

Means Productivity Standards for Construction. Third Edition. Kingston, MA: R.S. Means Co., 1994. (Formerly *Means Man-Hour Standards for Construction*.)
Contains productivity information for construction crews, equipment, and labor. Includes descriptions of each construction task, with many variations, detailed crew information and equipment requirements, and both daily output and labor-hours per unit.

Ramsey, Charles, and Sleeper, Harold. *Architectural Graphic Standards*. New York: Wiley, 1990 or later.
Try to get the residential edition that covers spacings for plumbing fixtures, minimum room sizes, stair design, etc.

The Wood Book. Tacoma, WA: Wood Product Publishing, 1978 and later.
Wood product data sheets from many national associations, all under one cover.

Cost Guides

Contractor's Pricing Guide: Residential Detailed Costs 1995. Kingston, MA: R.S. Means Co., 1994.
Includes unit costs for thousands of residential building components, daily productivity values, typical crew listings, and overhead and profit information.

Means Building Construction Cost Data 1995. Kingston, MA: R.S. Means Co., 1994.

    Provides unit prices covering all categories of construction, covering all 50 States and Canada. Also available in metric, in looseleaf form, and in a Western edition.

Means Square Foot Costs 1995. Kingston, MA: R.S. Means Co., 1994.

    Provides square foot costs for 100 basic buildings (residential, commercial, industrial, and institutional) and over 6,000 variations. Covers all 50 States and Canada.

Organizations

HALT (Help Stop American Legal Tyranny).
201 Massachusetts Avenue NE, Washington, DC 20002.

NAHB (National Organization of Home Builders).
15th & M Street NW, Washington, DC 20005.

Note: To take advantage of the floor plan review service offered by NAHB's Design Committee and Professional Builder *magazine described in Chapter 5, write to Pro Builder, 1350 E. Touhy Ave., Des Plaines, IL 60017-5080.*

Index

Notes

Notes

Notes

Notes